Why the New NHS will Fail

Why the New NHS will Fail:

And What Should Replace It?

Roger Dyson

Matthew James Publishing Ltd

First published in 2003
by
Matthew James Publishing Ltd
19 Wellington Close, Chelmsford, Essex CM1 2EE

ISBN 1898366 84 5

Cover design by Eclipse
Printed by J W Arrowsmith, Bristol

ACKNOWLEDGEMENTS

I am not able to name individually the many doctors, nurses, midwives and other clinicians who have shaped the analysis in this book over the last decade. And they may be glad of that! But I would like to thank in a more personal way those people who have given time and effort to correct and comment upon successive drafts of the book and to those who have produced it for me.

Dr Hugh Saxton a consultant radiologist who worked at Guy's Hospital and was Chairman of the Management Board there; Mr David Rosin consultant in upper GI and minimal access surgery at St Mary's Hospital, Dr Donald Woodgate consultant physician at Basildon and Thurrock NHS Hospitals Trust and Dr Ann Naylor consultant anaesthetist at the same hospital; both now retired from Basildon. None of them can be held responsible for any remaining errors, which are mine; and in particular the content of Chapter 5 which is entirely down to the author.

None of this work would have come to fruition, however, without the tireless efforts of Nikki Airey and Jackie Large who between them coped with tapes and handwriting with patience and good humour throughout. I owe them and my textual critics a great debt of gratitude. Finally I must also thank Peter Carter Ruck and Partners, solicitors, for their helpful assistance with the text.

Roger Dyson

September 2003

CONTENTS

PREFACE

For an academic whose special interest is health care I have had the good fortune to have been able to work at virtually every level of decision making and delivery in the UK NHS across a forty year career. By the end of the 1970s I was, or had been, an adviser on labour and employment issues to all the independent non-medical and dental professions in the NHS, and to doctors and scientists in pathology. From 1973 onwards I chaired Inquiries and was commissioned to undertake research reports at every level of the NHS and continued this work until my retirement in 2001. In the 1980s I was Chairman of a Health Authority; between 1979 and 1981 I was a consultant adviser to Patrick Jenkin the then Secretary of State in the Department of Health and Social Security; and for eleven years between 1986 and 1996 I taught health policy to the Cabinet Office programme for top civil servants. For the twenty years before my retirement I also taught senior/specialist registrars separately for each of the English Medical Royal Colleges. I was told on retirement that between 1995 and 2000 I had personally taught more than half the newly appointed NHS consultants in the UK.

My great good luck in having these opportunities was to a large extent due to the fact that in the early 1970s I was the only academic around who had done any work on NHS labour supply and labour management issues when a tidal wave of mainly unofficial strike action hit the NHS, between 1973 and 1982. Those of my labour economist colleagues who picked the car industry in the 1960s were high and dry by the mid 1980s, but health just kept on growing. Today there is an army of academic health economists in every branch of the discipline and the growth rate is truly astounding. Today I would simply not have had the opportunity to work and study so comprehensively across the NHS. Even in retirement I have been fortunate in becoming a county councillor. As Chairman of the Essex NHS Overview and Scrutiny Committee I am able to learn about and understand the realities of the NHS/Social Service interface which was a major blind spot during my academic career.

I have wanted to write this book at my retirement for over a decade but its content is very different from what I had expected in 1991. Despite this the two key objectives for writing have remained constant. Firstly, the process of debating and deciding upon the direction of UK health policy is one that only involves a narrow circle of people. It is closed not only to the population at large but also to the vast majority of professional and support staff who deliver health care day by day - people who constantly wonder why seemingly perverse and 'cockeyed' decisions are made and whose morale suffers in consequence. This 'closedness' is not created by the barriers of sapiental authority, - "we have the knowledge and you don't", - but by the determination that health policy will proceed by stealth in order to conceal its true direction. This is based upon the assumption that if the public knew where we were going they would oppose. This point is not party political. It applies equally to the Conservative Party White Paper in 1991 and to Alan Milburn's 'New NHS'. The first objective of this book is to try to put these policy issues into the public domain to encourage a wider, democratic debate about the right way forward and to advocate one particular policy direction.

The second objective is linked to the first. In 1995 one senior Whitehall mandarin told me that the trouble with my political party (I am a Conservative county councillor) was that it would never be allowed by the public to dismantle the NHS and re-build health care provision because it had not set up the NHS. "We will have to let the other lot back in, because only they can get away with market controls. When they've finished of course, *we'll* let your lot back!" Events have proved him right, the process is now well underway. This generous gesture in allowing Conservatives back in when market controls are established was probably due to a belief that, once established, Conservatives are better able to sustain a market economy. The second objective of the book is to demonstrate how this is being done. The subtle word "choice", first used in 1991, now dominates the 'New NHS'; 'Choice' will dismantle the universality of Bevan's NHS, and this same 'choice' will lock in the economic controls on future health provision. And 'choice' is too comforting a word for any one to object - until it is too late! So a supporter of free at the point of delivery health care like myself, has at least to try to offer a viable way of saving it, before 'choice' makes the debate redundant.

The content of the book that follows is aimed at achieving these two objectives by setting out why the 'New NHS' will fail and what should replace it. The book is therefore not a comprehensive study of the whole NHS because it selects the key issues and services crucial to the future of the 'New NHS'. The five chapters are structured as follows:

Chapter 1   debates issues of diversity, choice and inequality and considers the implications of the equality/diversity paradox in health care.

Chapter 2   is concerned with acute hospital provision; the changes in this aspect of health policy since 1991 and the current state and direction of the acute hospital service.

Chapter 3   analyses the seriousness and significance of the labour supply shortfall in the NHS; shows why it is *the* most significant factor in service failure, and why current policy initiatives will exacerbate rather than resolve the labour shortage.

xi

Chapter 4   looks at the health and social services divide, explains the growing difficulties that prevent a smooth service continuum across the divide and identifies where 'New NHS' methodologies are going to fail.

Chapter 5   sets out a framework and methodology for continuing to provide and develop a public health care system that is free at the point of delivery and re-establishes the traditional principles of equality of access and quality of service; something very different from the 'New NHS'.

All it will then need is a political party willing to establish it!

CHAPTER 1

THE NEW NHS AND THE EQUALITY/ DIVERSITY PARADOX

1 The New NHS

In 1997 Frank Dobson, the new Labour Secretary of State, inherited the Conservatives' health policy initiatives and direction established in the 1991 reforms. His approach to health policy was cautious and pragmatic, and was strongly influenced by the Chancellor of the Exchequer's wider decision to remain initially within Conservative funding assumptions. As a result many of the Conservatives' key health policy objectives (discussed in more detail in Chapters 2 and 3) continued apace between 1997 and 1999. It was the appointment of Alan Milburn as Secretary of State that triggered off a more radical re-direction of health policy and with hindsight it is reasonable to assume that the Prime Minister appointed him with a specific brief to get things moving in health. The result was that after a period of gestation Milburn launched his 'New NHS' at the beginning of 2002.

This book will demonstrate in some detail why this 'New NHS' constitutes an abandonment of the commitment to a universal and equitable health care system free at the point of delivery, available to all and funded out of taxation. It will show how diversity, or 'choice', is being used as a key change agent in securing a more limited public health provision which will in turn drive up the size of the population's own necessary private expenditure on health care with a resulting increase in inequality of access. Also, as with the Conservative Government's Reforms of 1991, the book will show that the real objectives of health policy are being imposed by stealth and that the government's public relations (PR) machine is actively creating a new language within health to mask its true intentions and avoid public awareness and concern. The book will conclude by offering an 'Alternative NHS' that returns to the principles of *equality* of access to a free health care service.

It can be argued, as with my Whitehall mandarin quoted in the Preface, that it was necessary to scale down the NHS and put limits on publicly funded access to health care. Also that only a Labour government can achieve this because the public will believe that the NHS is safe with Labour. It is certainly true that the capacity of the international health care industry to offer greater health benefits and opportunities is growing at a much faster rate than national economic growth. This imbalance looks set to continue at least in the short and medium term. There is the obvious concern that in a country where health is funded out of taxation the system will break down as public resistance to higher taxation grows; not to mention the detrimental effects on economic growth itself caused by rising levels of taxation. Only the price disciplines of a market, it is argued, can hold these forces in check and balance the extent of health care provision with the ability to pay.

The Blair government seems to have accepted this analysis. Its new Primary Care Trusts (PCTs) are to act as the agents of the market; they will have finite resources and can choose to buy, or not to buy, all the different bits of health care on offer from the market of public 'NHS' providers; from private sector providers; from the UK or abroad. In 'choosing' what to buy locally they will involve the public who therefore have 'choice' of what health care they get! What has been abandoned in this approach is the concept of a universal health care system offering access to a full range of health services, and crucially the concept of *equality* of access for all of the people of the UK. The 'Alternative NHS' offered in the final chapter of this book places equality of health provision and health access above choice in a system which makes rationing more explicit and understood rather than concealed and confusing.

In developing these arguments I begin with an example of the rhetoric of the 'New NHS'.

In a speech on, 'Redefining the National Health Service', released on January 15th, 2002, Alan Milburn said, "...the NHS is today implementing the biggest programme of change in its fifty year history." The old *national* health service was criticised and swept away to be replaced by a "..single national *health* service – an NHS of all the talents. One that puts its patients first." The old *national* health service is described as having been "...monolithic and bureaucratic , run like an old style nationalised industry (sic) controlled from Whitehall." The *old* system is seen in stark terms "...queuing is endemic...a system seeming to work for its own convenience not the patients...", in which "...patients are disempowered with little if any choice...Doctors were left in charge of providing limited services and patients were expected to be grateful for the limits of what they received...What we envisage is a fundamentally different sort of NHS."

The 'New NHS' is very different from the old and includes many features that would shock the founding fathers of 1946.

- Using private capital via the PFI (Private Finance Initiative) is praised, and is a cornerstone of national policy; the instrument that will deliver 100 new hospitals in a decade.

3

- NHS patients are now being treated in the private sector at special rates by private sector doctors and this is now a virtue of the system because it speeds access for the favoured NHS patients chosen for treatment.

- As an extension of the same new principle, NHS patients are being sent to hospitals overseas.

- New foundation hospitals are to have many freedoms to work in the way they choose, develop new services and expand others with money obtained by trading or other activities. They are also to have *more* money than other hospitals to reward their "success"

It is important to draw attention to the fact that the Government has achieved some slippage (six months) even in its first two years. The importance of this concern about deadlines is that slippage is dangerous for the government, because delay could come to be a significant factor in the failure of the 'New NHS'. The government cannot guarantee the delivery even of its own 'New NHS' because of serious supply side deficits of hospitals, beds, other facilities and crucially of professionally qualified staff. The government is faced with the task of delivering its 'New NHS' in working order fast enough to cope with growing demand against a background of inadequate and failing supply in the period before newly created facilities and newly trained staff are eventually available. The faster existing resources decline and the slower new resources are to materialise the greater the likelihood of a collapse of the whole system. For this reason slippage is fatal, which in part accounts for the current frenetic activity of government ministers and the growing frequency of new initiatives. This book will also argue that even if one were to accept that the government is going in the right policy direction their short term methodology is so flawed as to make the collapse of the whole system a very real possibility. It is for this reason that speed is of the essence and it is clear that the government is aware of this fact.

But to return to the discussion of the nature of the 'New NHS' it is necessary to explain the contradiction between the concept of equal access to, and availability of, health care and the idea of choice of health care as a collective decision of the local community. This is referred to below as the *equality/diversity paradox*.

2 The Equality / Diversity Paradox

There has always been a paradox in the NHS between the stated objective of *equality*; that is health care equally available to all according to their clinical need, and the *diversity* in the volume and range and quality of health care actually accessible to different sections of the population. But diversity as an *objective* of a free public service committed to equality heightens this paradox.

For the first fifty years of the NHS national policy initiatives sought to achieve greater equality in the provision of, and access to, health care and although most initiatives failed or were only partially successful there was never a serious challenge to the acceptance of an *equal* provision for *all* as an aim of a national public service.

Despite this, inequality has been rife at every level of the NHS during the entire period. There has been serious inequality of access to specialist tertiary services by distance, service volume and quality. There has been inequality in speed of access and of quality for major secondary services and diagnostic support. The presence or absence of capable clinicians with facilities to provide a good service has been a lottery and the lack of choice in accessing A&E departments an even greater one. The presence or absence of a Nursing Home and the accessibility of a Residential Home has probably been the greatest lottery in social support. Even in the allocation of health funding there is gross inequality with Scotland on 8.1% of GDP in 2002 and England on 6.3%.

5

The important point about all this inequality is that for most of the period public opinion was either quiescent or limited to a low level of traditional grumbling of the wartime shortages type that focussed upon general insufficiency rather than upon inequality of availability. The debate *within* the NHS about the allocation of resources and facilities never really gripped the public and there was little serious attempt by politicians to 'take the debate to the people'. Rather, the debate was an internal matter for the cognoscenti, and the role of a Secretary of State was to defend his/her department and those who worked in the NHS from periodic and often uninformed attacks by MPs. To add to this neither the Department of Health nor the NHS itself collected statistics that would be informative in any serious debate about inequality with the exception of generalised waiting lists, deaths and discharges.

Virginia Bottomley was the first Secretary of State who began to change the rules, though her motives may not have been entirely altruistic. By the late 1980s 'Health' was not viewed with enthusiasm by an ambitious MP. Increasingly the job involved defending a service from detailed attacks on specific patient related problems with the mood of the House ranging from hostile to silent. Virginia Bottomley found a route to political survival, knowingly or otherwise, by using the Patients Charter of 1991 and attacking the NHS even more aggressively than other MPs for not achieving it. Not all subsequent Secretaries of State followed this example, but in New Labour this technique has reached its apotheosis! Those who work in the service can be forgiven for believing that the 'thought police' walk down every corridor in the NHS. This significant change in the direction and political management of the NHS has had at least two consequences.

- Starting with Virginia Bottomley's use of the Patients Charter we now have a very substantial number of codes and targets in the NHS. They cover the government's favoured clinical targets of cancer, heart disease, mental health and the generic issue of the elderly. They extend across a wide range of specific target dates for accessing major sections of the NHS. They even get into matters of day to day behaviour, such as how clinicians function together in teams, and we now have league tables of individual consultant's performances within certain specialties.

These targets and the substantial increase in comparative data have certainly stimulated the public's discontent with the NHS. Not only is there the usual concern with inadequacy and delay (now supported by much more detailed data), there is also a totally new awareness of how great is the inequality in the distribution of services across the UK – due to the league tables. Indeed the government can fairly be accused of exaggerating the downside and the inequality – "due to 18 years of Tory neglect", in the hope of contrasting this with the perfect NHS to be achieved by Labour. There is a clear political danger in this approach!

• The second consequence, already visible, is the negative effect on staff morale that all this publication of data and encouraging of greater public dissatisfaction has engendered. Exposure of comparative performance within an organisation is one thing, but exposure of comparative performance to the whole world including one's neighbours and friends is much worse for the individual.

The tidal wave of ill thought through statistics has affected NHS staff morale adversely. This has had a negative effect on the ability to retain and recruit scarce staff. Those who work in the NHS have the right to say, 'give us a proper hospital, give us the right equipment and the staff to deliver a better service'; but the government's recognition of this at the macro-level does nothing to relieve low morale at the micro-level.

7

The major investment assured by Gordon Brown has been helpful to morale, but it is now factored into the morale level of the service and there is unlikely to be another such investment. It was a single major decision, but from now on "events" will keep pulling in the opposite direction because the flow of government data and public response will be continuous. Gordon Brown may try to re-invent the same investment statistics on an annual basis, but the public is getting wise to this type of spin – and has become cynical.

One defence of the government's major increase in performance measurement and publicity is that this had to be done to start off the process of reform and to explain all the changes to the public. Unfortunately the failure to understand and resolve the equality/diversity paradox has led to a confused and contradictory set of initiatives.

When one looks at the range of policy initiatives in the last four years it is hard to believe that the government understands the significance of the equality/diversity paradox. Uniform and equitable access to services are stressed many times. It has been implied that no recipient of cervical cytology screening should ever have a mis-read smear. Everyone is supposed to be entitled to a correct report, a view reinforced in a recent legal judgement despite the inexact nature of the science. NICE (the National Institute of Clinical Excellence) has promised to end postcode prescribing and beyond just pharmaceuticals there is a clear impression given that all postcode variations are unacceptable. The promise of free nursing care in nursing homes was not announced alongside an explanation that this was only for those lucky enough to live in parts of the country where there were nursing homes and so the implication of equality of treatment was again emphasised.

All this contrasts sharply with the many initiatives that encourage diversity. At the centre are PCTs, that control NHS resources, and are to determine with various patient groups like Patients Forums, the Commission for Public and Patient Involvement in Health (CPPIH), and patient/carer pressure groups, the *different* priorities of their PCTs (when these formal bodies are finally operational from December 2003). These PCTs are to exist alongside a growing number of Foundation Trusts; primarily acute hospitals that will win the right for substantial freedom within the NHS to determine their own agenda and priorities including becoming more involved in the private sector. Significantly Foundation Trusts are to get *more* resources than other Trusts *because they perform better!* This is the very antithesis of striving for equality of provision in a public service. There are many other offers of diversity; in mental health and in many sectors of primary care. The government appear to have played the diversity or equality presentations quite ad hoc. This has created confusion about the precise objectives of national policy and has hidden the key role of 'choice' as the methodology for re-constructing a different and more limited health care system.

The Kings Fund discussion document, "The Future of the NHS : A Framework for Debate", published in January 2002, concluded very prophetically and accurately that, "...the NHS was founded on the notion of equity of access, and a key objective of the service is to provide equal access to care for patients, in equal need. Increasing choice can conflict with this goal." Sadly, having correctly stated the paradox the Report ignores it in favour of decentralised choice and diversity without admitting or considering the implications of ending the commitment to equity.

Why is the equality/diversity paradox so important? Firstly, as indicated above, by putting so much diversity data into the public domain Labour has helped to stir up more public dissatisfaction, which in many different ways increases the potential for failure in the 'New NHS'. The government's obvious frustration with this indicates either a lack of understanding of what the paradox is or,

9

if understood, an enormous risk that is time limited, needing success before the arrival of a systems failure. The frenetic pace of government 'activity' in health may suggest the latter interpretation. But if it is genuinely understood the circle of knowledge is likely to be very small. Secondly, and much more important, diversity and choice can only be viable in a national public service if both supply and variety are sufficient to meet public demand for all of the people, in all of the UK. In the NHS today there is a huge imbalance between supply and demand and no hope, as yet, that local choice can be anything more than a device directed towards hiding rather than focusing upon the supply/demand imbalances. These imbalances extend right across the health service to hospitals, their facilities, clinical staffing, access to GPs etc, etc. What does any good government do when there is a major public service imbalance caused by lack of supply? It rations the service. And what does a socially acceptable national rationing system require? It requires strict equity of provision. The refusal of all politicians in government to use the forbidden word, 'rationing', means that there is never a sensible discussion about the implications of the supply/demand imbalance. Instead this issue is being smothered under a smokescreen of diversity with local choice; a policy option uniquely suited to maximise public discontent when the public come to see local *choice* as merely sacrificing Peter to pay for Paul, a principle well understood by economists, but not one that is immediately attractive to local communities. But by that time it may well be too late to change back.

Wartime food rationing provides a good analogy for the present supply shortages. In a bid for popularity the Labour Government withdrew sweet rationing in the late 1940s before there was an adequate supply and *choice*. The resulting discontent and profiteering forced them quickly to restore rationing. If we go for diversity in the NHS, as the government has done, there should be adequate supply

10

and genuine choice. In crucial areas; e.g. adequate and accessible A&E services, adequate and timely access to medical consultants; to diagnostic interventions, and the availability of Nursing Homes, there is a manifest lack of adequate supply; which makes a sham of genuine choice. Diversity and choice is a luxury that is achieved when adequate supply is available. It is a wholly legitimate goal, but its *immediate* introduction via Primary Care Trusts (PCTs) and their Patients Forums cannot hope to deliver unless universality is sacrificed. Patients will find out that it is, ". . . this *or* that . . .", and if it's "this" you either pay for "that" or you go without. Out of this will come public dissatisfaction not patience; confusion rather than understanding. Politicians used to be accused of always offering jam tomorrow. The criticism here is that they are now offering jam today when there is clearly not enough jam to go round.

Even if supply and demand were more in balance, the offer of diversity and choice in a 'free at the point of delivery' public service would be fraught with difficulty. We already have parents fighting for housing in the catchment area of state schools with better levels of achievement. Imagine the much more daunting prospect of this happening in health. Suppose the mental health lobby achieves considerable success in some PCTs in funding community mental health services and access to acute beds, relative to other PCTs; or that the same was achieved by the stroke patients' pressure group in another PCT. This could cause people to move house, but not only that, among those who cannot move, it will increase discontent with the 'inequality' (i.e. not their preference) of health provision that will not be resolved simply by an addition to general funding. It is these 'inequalities' that will drag national politicians back into individual cases again and again no matter how much they hope to distance themselves.

The public accepts that in private matters, like the purchase of a car, choice is limited by available funds; as a result of which some will choose a Rolls Royce and some a Fiat Uno without rioting in the streets. In a free at the point of delivery health care system any open variation in provision within the NHS will cause public dissatisfaction, even the variation between good and excellent. Encouraging patients to battle at PCT level for local choice as to local priorities will result in 'losers' as well as 'winners'. The losers will go to their MPs, their MPs will go to the Secretary of State. Choice would only be really workable when *individual* patients make clinical choices for *themselves* after receiving clinical advice in the knowledge of all the available options; but that gets us back to equality and universality, with open rationing if supply is inadequate. This would mean money genuinely following the patient and if and when this is achieved we will not need PCTs. This line of argument demonstrates that PCTs are a rationing device, as was/is the gatekeeper role of the GP. Diversity and local choice in PCTs merely means that patient pressure groups can contest with professional staff about how this gatekeeper role is exercised. This is very different from the assumed diversity and choice for GPs and patients in the official literature, primarily because the supply/demand imbalance is ignored and the definition of 'choice' as the economists' 'choice' is not explained. Patients still believe 'choice' means that, "I can have what I think I need."

There is a very seductive view that if new money is available in sufficient quantity supply will grow faster than demand and that genuine equality and individual choice will be achieved without rationing. Gordon Brown's large new investment and the debate about winning hearts and minds for higher taxation for health has encouraged this delusion. This view fails to recognise how deeply health inequality is embedded into the NHS. There is within the system an amazingly strong capacity for those with the greatest resources to command the bulk of new money. The government's recent concern about its inability to ring fence and deliver cancer cash is just one aspect of this capacity. The radical reform that is really

12

needed is to destroy this capacity in order to prevent new resources merely being squandered to bolster and expand existing inequalities. (Foundation Trusts are an excellent example of bolstering existing inequalities.) To explain exactly how this works in practice, however, it is necessary to provide a fully explained case study and this is set out below.

3 Why Extra Funding can Bolster Inequality (A Glasgow case study)

After 1997 I was involved in assisting the attempt to rationalise the Glasgow pathology service and reduce its high level of expenditure. The Glasgow Health Board served an immediate population of a little over 900,000, plus inward referrals at an annual pathology service cost of £40.5 million. By contrast Leicestershire Health Authority served an immediate population of over1,000,000, with somewhat fewer inward referrals at an annual pathology service cost of £16 million. Both authorities had major teaching hospitals. Even within Scotland the Glasgow health funding is a living legend and this despite its genuine case for some better funding to recognise its unique social morbidity. But this was not the *principal* cause of the huge pathology budget. Glasgow had six separate full acute hospitals at a population ratio of only 150,000. Three of these were traditional teaching hospitals and one claimed to be. Each hospital averaged four to seven separate departmental pathology sub-specialties, and the total Glasgow pathology resources and staffing were greater than the Wessex and also the East Anglian English Regions.

Glasgow needs *one* city wide adult microbiology department to improve the quality of its service; three adult acute histopathology departments would have done the same, and the total adult acute health service should have been rationalised onto at most, three sites. It will not surprise the reader to learn that there is no political will nationally, in Scotland or in Glasgow, to address the problem other than with the gentlest of tentative incremental footsteps over the medium and longer term. Outside Glasgow, and to a lesser extent Edinburgh, Scotland has an enormous inequality in health provision resulting from a gross monopoly of resources by the 'hubs' (the two major clinical centres) over many years leading to genuinely under-resourced and under-developed district hospital 'spokes'.

In case any readers are still puzzled, the explanation can be taken further. The Scottish health service is *hugely* dominated by Glasgow and to a lesser extent Edinburgh. Over the years their senior clinicians, academics, chief executives, politicians, trade union branches, etc, have wielded enormous power to ensure that new money comes to them and that resources do not get properly re-distributed, despite a large number of medium and longer term initiatives to do just that. Pathology provides an example of this. In the late 1990s the then Chief Medical Officer for Scotland set up a Working Party to determine how to measure and fund pathology work.

When a specimen, eg blood or urine, comes to a clinical pathology department to be processed it is called a 'request' and constitutes demand on laboratory services. The laboratory carries out a varied series of automated or manual 'tests' to produce diagnostic results; the requests each constitute demand on the laboratory to produce diagnostic results; the test results each constitute supply. It is for the pathology department to determine how many 'tests' are to be performed. Some equipment performs more automated tests than others, and some tests involve varying amounts of re-agent costs. Throughout the UK, outside Scotland, the request is taken as the unweighted measure of laboratory workload for funding and performance measurement. In Scotland the Working Party recommended the test instead, i.e. funding and performance measurement based on self-determined supply! Glasgow has the clinicians, the staff, and the equipment, to undertake enormous numbers of tests for each request, something that under-staffed and

14

under-equipped peripheral Scottish hospital laboratories cannot hope to match. Glasgow has thus been offered long-term guarantees of resources and protection. The result is greater inequality; funding by test is unique to Scotland and the tragedy for the NHS is that all the extra tests are of no value to the patient other than the standard and specious defence that once in a blue moon an unrelated disease is spotted.

The reason why this inequality in pathology, and the much wider one of Scottish inequality in the provision of secondary and tertiary acute hospital services exists is the lack of *political* will. Those who provide Glasgow's pathology and reinforce Glasgow's six major acute hospitals have allies of great determination and strength – the population of Glasgow. "These are our hospitals, our pathology departments, our consultants and other people may be allowed to use them *provided* they travel to Glasgow." The Glasgow NHS establishment has played on this threat of public anger to prevent reform on countless occasions, with two results.

- Many parts of Scotland get an inferior and unequal service, even by standards in the rest of the UK.

- Even the people of Glasgow, and those referred in, risk a less beneficial service because of small competing and overlapping clinical services more concerned with defending their territory than with city-wide co-operation in the modernisation of clinical services.

This situation exists despite Glasgow's NHS funding being in excess of Scotland's 8.1% GDP average.

Seriously tackling inequality and the waste it produces is not assured by a major increase in national funding; if anything inequality is reinforced unless radical action is taken. This is why

Gordon Brown's new funding gets drawn into black holes with no apparent benefit to national health care. New money alone does not solve problems, and as Glasgow indicates it can actually *increase* inequality. Unfortunately the government's commitment to a new 'hub' and 'spoke' acute hospital strategy (see Chapter 2) seems likely to further reinforce the 'benefit' to Glasgow rather than to remedy it.

4 Conclusion

The greatest tragedy of Gordon Brown's new funding is that it will be squandered in reinforcing inequality of access to and provision of health care across the UK. Not only will the structural problems of inequality be ignored, but the emphasis upon choice, upon 'backing winners' like foundation trusts, upon backing the best clinical teams etc, will indeed increase the unequal provision of health care and for this reason alone the 'New NHS' cannot, in the end, succeed. Better managers and better clinicians are one reason for better trusts and better outcomes; but so are better resources, more facilities; more staff; up to date systems etc; these never get factored into deciding where resources should go. If they were, equality would demand that new resources go to the under-staffed, the under-equipped, the hospitals with out-dated and collapsing systems etc. This starkly illustrates the black and white alternatives of Labour's 'New NHS' and the 'Alternative NHS' outlined in Chapter 5.

CHAPTER 2

ACUTE AND ELECTIVE
HOSPITAL SERVICES

In this chapter we look at the acute hospital and specialist services which form so large a component of the NHS. Community hospitals and so-called intermediate care beds, though vital to the future healthcare system, are more appropriately discussed later in the context of the continuum between the health and social services.

1 A Patchwork of Hospitals 1946 - 1991

The 1946 Act which established the NHS brought into a single structure a variety of different hospitals: teaching hospitals run by Boards of Governors, independent voluntary hospitals, workhouse hospitals run by local authorities together with cottage and maternity hospitals and other specialist institutions. Not only were these of widely differing standard but their distribution bore no relation to the size of the local population. In many cases hospital services had tended to develop in more affluent communities where the majority of available doctors were attracted to practice. Charitable provision by local industries and hospital collections by the stronger trade unions had done something to alleviate the imbalance of resources but in 1946 it was still significant. Some teaching hospitals in London had been based in very deprived areas and then found the local population diminishing as poor housing was cleared in the decades after the War.

One factor that stifled a response to this imbalance was the presence of private practice in central London. Thus, in the 1960s and 1970s, when it became clear that the population around London teaching hospitals was dwindling, there were those who advocated moving some of the hospitals to the more populous areas in outer London. This was strongly resisted by the hospital consultants who did not want to move so far from their private rooms. Only St. George's Hospital and the Royal Free Hospital took the opportunity to base themselves in areas where there were larger numbers of patients with the common disorders most suitable for demonstration to students.

Access to specialist and tertiary services

There has always been confusion in the use of the terms 'specialist' and 'tertiary', even if professionals have no doubts. In this book secondary hospital care in acute hospitals is provided by generalist consultants with appointments such as general surgeons and general physicians and by specialists like cardiologists and urologists etc. *Any* clinical service provided in a secondary local hospital can be 'generalist' or 'specialist' but is not 'tertiary'. 'Tertiary' services are those where the degree of sub-specialisation limits demand and where complexity means that only a limited number of hospitals will offer the service. Most of these 'tertiary' services are offered within major secondary hospital services such as teaching hospitals. Over time wider access to a 'tertiary' service can result in it becoming primarily a 'specialist' service offered at secondary hospital level, e.g., renal dialysis.

In the early years of the NHS it was accepted that if patients needed most specialist and all *tertiary* services this involved going to a teaching hospital which might involve them in travelling long distances. Those able to reach these hospitals had better healthcare, so in London and the major cities, health provision was better. This is not to say that there were no pockets of deprivation in London and the main provincial cities, but in general better access meant better care.

In the first 40 years of the NHS this inequality of provision was somewhat reduced. In the early 1960s Enoch Powell, as Minister of Health, introduced the concept of the district general hospital (DGH). He initiated what ultimately became a pattern of DGHs across many parts of the country – built mainly between the mid – 60s and 70s – which provided acute and elective hospital services. Moreover, as time went on and well-trained senior registrars became consultants in such hospitals, it became somewhat less necessary to travel far for specialist services except those dealing with less common conditions.

Even so, the assumption remained that some specialist services would be provided at the bigger secondary acute hospitals whilst for smaller and medium sized acute hospitals they would be provided at the very unevenly distributed 'tertiary' teaching hospitals. From the beginning of the 1980s successive Secretaries of State made formal attempts to introduce more equity in the allocation of resources between Regions, using population and standardised mortality ratios as a proxy for morbidity levels. Progress was desperately slow as those who had the resources, and the backing of powerful professional interests, fought a long and sometimes successful battle against any significant redistribution between or within Regions.

As an example, even in the mid-1980s, as Chairman of the North Staffordshire Health Authority, I was involved in repeated bitter arguments with the West Midlands RHA because of the marked imbalance in the distribution of resources between Birmingham and most other parts of the Region. The Regional Chairman and Administrator argued that complex clinical services should be concentrated in central Birmingham and that the whole of the region should travel to access these 'tertiary' services. Similar conflicts were being fought out to a greater or less extent throughout the country. Much of south east England in the four Thames Regions was expected to access services in central London for the same reason.

What is being argued in this opening historical summary is that in 1946 the NHS began with *substantial* inequality in the distribution of secondary and tertiary hospital services and that between 1946 and 1991 the major policy initiatives to reduce this inequality were at best only partially successful. With the exception of Enoch Powell's DGHs the results were quite meagre, even in the case of the 1977 Resource Allocation Working Party, (RAWP) in England. This was primarily because the well resourced centres not only fought against re-distribution, but also for a large slice of any new resources invested. This even *increased* inequality of access to services because when the Thames Regions' funding grew at a less rapid rate the main squeeze was on secondary hospitals out of London; and the same happened in Scotland and elsewhere. Preserving (ie growing) the centres of excellence was and is a powerful cry, always fully backed up by the local population and its political leadership. Against this background greater equality remained the formally stated public policy but few national politicians had the strength or will to tackle powerful local vested interests.

2 The Thatcher Reforms 1991 – 1997

This last major attempt to radically reform the pattern of hospital provision came with the Conservative Government's White Paper Implementation of 1991. Work on these reforms was initiated by Margaret Thatcher in the late 1980s and was put in place by Kenneth Clarke as Secretary of State. Even now it is too early to unravel fully the network of interests and objectives that led to the policy details, but enough is now known to understand most of the fundamentals. The key factors in the policy development and its aftermath are set out below.

The late 1980s was a period when relationships between the government and the BMA were not good and the medical Royal Colleges were both the obvious and the only source of medical clinical advice for ministers and senior civil servants. The Chief Medical Officer (CMO) at the Department of Health (DOH) had always appointed an eminent consultant from each major specialty as his advisor on the specialty. For the first 50 years of the NHS these posts have overwhelmingly been held by senior officers of medical Royal Colleges. As will be shown, individual Royal Colleges already had a clear vision of what was required in hospital development in order to support a series of necessary clinical developments that focussed upon quality issues. Much of what the Royal Colleges wanted was part of a series of policy initiatives linked to and developing from the 1991 Reforms, but government's acceptance of much of the Royal Colleges' objectives brought its embarrassments. The Colleges were and are non-political, there was a desire *not* to be publicly associated with radical change and a view that it was the role of government to handle the political fallout. So the government went ahead in 1991 with a policy that substantially reduced the number of secondary acute hospitals without a clear statement of, or national *open* professional support for, its clinical rationale. This reduction in hospital numbers resulted from several key initiatives all moving in the same direction.

The Clinical Rationale

Contrary to popular belief there was a significant clinical rationale for the 1991 reforms. The issues are listed below.

A Medical Training Needs and Hospital Size

During the early 1990s Dr. Kenneth Calman (the CMO) presided over a major change in the organisation and structure of hospital medical training. He worked very closely with the medical Royal Colleges over a two to three year period to introduce significant change.

One of the important health successes of the Major Government was its drive to increase substantially the number of medical

21

consultants working in the UK. This was needed both to respond to growing demand and to shift the balance between generalist and specialist hospital medical consultants, so as to respond to the growing emphasis placed upon specialist medical consultant services. An increase in the number of consultants takes time and the details of this operation are considered in the next chapter. Its relevance to *this* chapter is that by merging the two career posts of registrar and senior registrar into one new career post of specialist registrar (SpR) it reduced training time. This was reinforced by giving higher medical trainees a guaranteed fixed date when they became eligible for a consultant appointment. This policy was certainly successful in enabling the consultant body to expand. **But what is the significance of this issue to the question of hospital size?**

The medical Royal Colleges had to ensure that the quality of training in each year of training was improved and was more closely monitored in order to ensure that the final product at the end of training was a doctor fit to take a consultant post. This meant that medical trainees could only work in a hospital environment where they were exposed to enough clinical material to acquire the necessary clinical competences.

To give some examples, in accident and emergency (A&E) the minimum required number of annual attendances was increased if hospital departments were to have a trainee. In obstetrics and gynaecology the obstetric unit had to have a minimum of 3,000 deliveries a year for the same reason. In paediatrics there was an increased minimum number of inpatients in hospitals where SpRs were to be based for training. To take just one surgical example there was a new target for the minimum number of vascular surgeons that had to be employed before they could have trainees. The effect of all this was the gradual withdrawal of services from smaller to medium sized hospitals because without their trainees to cover the weekend and night time work at an appropriate level of trainee seniority it was no longer either viable or safe for the service to continue to be provided.

An increasing number of hospitals were affected by this withdrawal. One enthusiast, Professor Roy Meadow the President of the Royal College of Paediatrics and Child Health, claimed that one of his objectives was to withdraw training from a significant proportion of the hospitals that had traditionally trained in paediatrics. All these illustrations indicate the implications of the Calman training changes for the pattern of hospital provision around the UK, because with the trainees directed elsewhere, full 24 hour acute services were virtually impossible to maintain in hospitals which had lost them.

One development has tempered the pace of the change. Some hospitals worked increasingly with non-training grades of staff in the medical career post of staff grade (now non-consultant career grade) to deliver the clinical service. A high proportion of staff grades were doctors who trained abroad and, whilst not having the qualifications to apply for a consultant post, were qualified to apply as staff grades. The reality, however, was that this leavening of the medical team in hospitals, committed to a heavier night time and weekend programme, only worked at those hospitals able to retain at least a core of SpR trainees. This issue is considered further in the next chapter.

The commitment of the medical Royal Colleges to hospital medical training reform in the early 1990s and their knowledge that this would reduce the number of acute hospital sites at which medical trainees worked was a key element in the clinical rationale of the 1991 reforms. It was also chronologically the first in a series of initiatives that drove the reduction in acute status for a growing number of smaller hospitals.

B Specialist Cancer Service

Today's reader may be forgiven for thinking that the Blair Government initiative on cancer services was something new. It is a characteristic of our adversarial political system that no party ever acknowledges or praises the work of another party. Labour have finessed the fact that the current cancer initiatives began in 1995 with the Report chaired by Dr. Calman (CMO), "A Policy Framework for Commissioning Cancer Services".

In this first initiative on cancer three types of cancer; colorectal, breast and lung cancer, were chosen for a pilot policy initiative to improve the quality of cancer outcomes. To use colorectal cancer as the illustration, the policy involved having a minimum of two colorectal cancer specialists working together in the same hospital each undertaking a minimum of procedures and attempting to offer a continuous service with improved access times for patients. The clinical evidence underpinning this change came from research undertaken by Professor Hardcastle at Nottingham University. Professor Hardcastle had shown in a series of longitudinal surveys of outcome in the Trent Region and in Wales, that there was sufficient data to indicate that surgeons performing a larger number of colorectal procedures had better long-term outcomes. The implementation of the Calman Cancer Report was based upon an acceptance of Professor Hardcastle's findings, which were then applied to a number of other types of cancer, (but not always with the same degree of separate and rigorous research).

For the purposes of this book the significant outcome of Professor Hardcastle's work was the conclusion that the number of colorectal procedures that should be undertaken in any one year by an individual surgeon should not fall below a defined minimum. The effect this had on DGHs was that some just did not have enough cancer in their smaller populations to allow two surgeons to achieve a viable workload. The implication is that if surgeons continue to do small quantities of work in smaller hospitals it will reduce the quality of the service to patients with a higher proportion of less satisfactory outcomes. Thus, some surgical work began to transfer to larger DGHs.

The more that surgical procedures are taken from the smaller to medium sized hospitals, the less viable the hospitals later become. The argument for a smaller number of larger hospitals grows because the larger hospitals have an adequate catchment population with an appropriate volume of clinical demand.

C Medical consultant numbers and hospital sizes

The need for fewer, larger hospitals was not just tied to the needs of high quality medical training. It was also linked to the issue of consultant numbers, the numbers required in any *one* team in any *one* hospital, to ensure the delivery of higher standards. As the success of the 1991 policy initiative became more assured, with a continuing fall in the number of 24 hour acute hospitals, the medical Royal Colleges became more open in their willingness to discuss the final shape of hospital services in the UK. Before considering examples of this it is now important to define what 'success' means in this context.

Between 1991 and 2001 the number of 24 hour full acute hospitals in the NHS declined from a little over 400 to below 300. In a decade full acute status was withdrawn from over a quarter of all hospitals. The key definition is that of 'acute' hospital. By this is meant a hospital open for 24 hours a day, seven days a week, offering a wide range of secondary acute services as well as in-patient elective surgery and perhaps other clinical services. It is hard to define the national number precisely because a small number of single specialty acute hospitals is included in the analysis and there is no unanimity about the categorisation of some hospitals. Of the hospitals that lost acute status during the decade the vast majority are still NHS hospitals but their use has changed, perhaps to become specialist hospitals in e.g., radiotherapy and oncology, perhaps to become community hospitals or hospitals providing intermediate care beds and a range of diagnostic and outpatient services etc., etc.,. During this period of rationalisation the surviving hospitals have been those secondary care hospitals with large enough support populations to develop their roles as providers of specialist medical services. This process of rationalisation has not been completed and will be considered again later in the chapter.

To return to the issue of consultant numbers the Royal College of Physicians of London produced the first published contribution to the debate in September 1996 in the document, "Future Patterns of Care by General and Specialist Physicians." This report considered that a team of six general physicians was necessary for a modern acute hospital to continue to provide general medical take (the rota of responsibility for *all* acute medical admissions on a daily basis) and that this team should also be a part of a larger consultant physician team which included a minimum of two consultants in each of the major physician specialties. One key conclusion of this report was that a population of at least 250,000 would be necessary in the longer term to resource and provide appropriate clinical volume for this team. Taking the UK as a whole this would mean a target acute hospital system of around 240 hospitals with perhaps a small extra number for the areas of very low population density.

Less than a year later, in June 1997 the Royal College of Surgeons of England produced, "The Provision of Emergency Surgical Services – an Organisational Framework." The surgeons went much further than the physicians and challenged the viability of a population base of only a quarter of a million. Surgeons argued that in the medium and longer term the role of general surgeon would shrink and that surgery would become an alliance of surgical specialties. This was necessary to continue to improve the quality of surgical outcomes. There would be a major clinical benefit to the patient if those surgical specialties could be grouped together to avoid patient transfer and to ensure timely involvement where the patient's condition was multi-factorial. The need to have vascular surgery as one of the core surgical specialties present in each 24 hour acute hospital was a crucial part of the College's analysis, and the final result of all this was support for a population base of 450,000 to half a million. Allowing for areas of low density population the surgical model would give only 150 or 160 acute hospitals for the whole of the UK. Nevertheless the reasoning was entirely based upon the quality of the clinical service to patients.

The reader should be aware that these thoughts about the future provision of acute hospital care, published in 1996/97, were very much a part of senior medical College membership thinking at the beginning of the 1990s. Powerful individual voices in many Colleges did, and a few still do, speak against the logic of this case. But the groundswell of opinion that eventually led to these reports of the mid 1990s had begun to influence senior civil servants at the beginning of the decade. It is clear that the medical Royal Colleges were thinking in terms of consultant teams that would be incompatible with the myriad of large, medium and small acute hospitals that were still functioning in 1990. And it explains, therefore, why reducing hospital numbers was one of the key outcomes of the 1991 strategy.

D Using Medical Consultant Cover at Night
The Confidential Enquiry into Perioperative Deaths (CEPOD) Report, "Who Operates When?", studied peri-operative deaths between the 1st April 1995 and the 31st March 1996. To condense

a much larger argument, more people were dying when the emergency, trauma and acute surgical work was undertaken in hospitals at nights and weekends by trainee doctors 'supervised' at a distance by consultants available on the telephone, than when consultants undertook the work. This CEPOD report recommended the employment of consultant teams in hospitals at night to undertake the acute trauma/surgical work in order to improve surgical outcomes. To justify the employment and cost of a nighttime consultant team it is necessary to have a sufficient volume of genuinely emergency demand and this requires a higher population base. To have employed such consultant teams at night across all the large, medium and small acute hospitals of the 1980s would have been impossible in terms of the number of consultants required and would have been a huge cost relative to the volume of work undertaken. Again, however, this need to improve the quality of clinical outcomes was driving the move towards a smaller number of larger acute hospitals and with it a greater equality of access to more guaranteed quality services.

E Consultant Appointments

In 1996 the Conservative Government introduced legislation to control the way in which consultants were appointed. This legislation became operative on the 1st January 1997 and included a requirement that the post and the person appointed be acceptable to the medical Royal College responsible for training, (and for the recognition of trained staff through its recommendations to a body called the Specialist Training Authority (STA) which registered trained medical staff for consultant work in the UK). As an example the Royal College of Surgeons of England started to refuse to recognise single handed consultant vascular surgeons whether or not they had trainees because a single handed service was considered to be clinically unsafe. This further strengthened the move away from smaller acute hospitals for 'at risk' patients.

28

The Economic Rationale

The economic rationale for the Tory reforms of 1991 does not need such a detailed explanation because it was well known and set out at the time and is not a matter of controversy.

This clinical rationalisation of the hospital system went hand in hand with expanded clinical capacity. To this extent the economic rationale of the 1991 policy initiatives was an attempt to place the greater financial cost of rising quality and rising specialisation into a manageable framework. Overlaid on this cost management initiative were a series of proposals to use NHS resources more effectively in delivering healthcare. If there is one theme that has united *all* politicians it has been the attraction of the argument that *existing* resources could be better used to improve healthcare delivery.

In 1991 the public theme of the re-organisation was **decentralisation.** The hospital trusts that were created were to have more freedom to use their resources to respond to patient demand. In particular they had more freedom to appoint the medical consultants they needed to meet demand. Similarly the new style Health Authorities were given broad health objectives and had freedom to use their resources flexibly in response to local demand and to tackle service weaknesses in their area. This theme of decentralisation also applied to GPs whose opportunities for 'fund-holding status' were intended to give them the freedom to use their budgets more imaginatively and to generate income that could be applied to local patient services.

Political opposition to the 1991 reforms focussed solely upon their perceived economic rationale. Trust hospitals were perceived, quite wrongly, as an attempt to introduce some form of privatisation into the NHS and senior medical and political figures formed the NHS Federation to fight against the changes. A key reason for the Federation's failure was that it did not understand the reforms and in picking 'trusts' as its target it chose the ground on which it was easiest for the government to defend. But if the Federation did not understand the *clinical* rationale and its effects why did not the government make a clear statement of its objectives? The answer, and the key to really understanding the 1991 reforms, lies in what has been called the political rationale.

The Political Rationale – a covert operation

In 1991/2 I was a strong advocate of going public with the clinical rationale and explaining why it required a reduction in the number of acute hospitals. The logic was overwhelming and the case could not lose! I was told by one civil service mandarin that I was a typical academic living in an ivory tower with no sense of political reality. The mandarin was of course right and his argument is set out below.

If the Secretary of State announced the full intentions of the 1991 reforms to the House of Commons, stating the reasons why this would involve reducing the number of acute hospitals in the UK, MPs would have only one question; "what is to happen to my constituency hospital(s)? " Every MP in a constituency that might lose one or more of its *acute* hospital(s) would vote against their own Party on a matter of local interest (even against a three line whip) and all opposition parties would be whipped against the policy. The result would be that the Major Government's 'majority' would simply not carry the policy.

To achieve this success the 1991 reforms therefore required secrecy. The hospital reduction scheme had to be achieved without people knowing that this was the policy and where, when it happened, the blame could be clearly deflected elsewhere. The mechanism devised by civil servants that achieved this was simple and quite brilliant. It was to divide health authorities from their hospitals on the back of the decentralisation initiative. Health authorities were given a degree of freedom to determine the health priorities of their population and to achieve those priorities, within budget, in whatever way they felt best.

30

Hospitals suddenly became independent, as hospital trusts, with the freedom to contract with one or more health authorities and the GP fundholders to raise income and to develop their own clinical services. Health authorities could no longer instruct the hospitals, but had to negotiate contracts with them. This device disguised the 'hospitals' issue in two ways.

❖ On average health authorities were responsible for contracting with between two and three different acute hospital trusts, and the health authorities had to deliver acute services with a finite annual budget. Without any prompting (which was essential if an unstated initiative is to succeed) those health authorities, one by one, began to realise that the concentration of their acute services from three down to two hospitals, or from two to one, would enable them better to deliver the clinical quality required. It would also be more in line with their budget. Different health authorities faced more or less immediate pressure to do this and the result was that instead of all health authorities coming forward at the same time with a similar initiative, their actions were spaced out in the following six years and were still continuing at the time of the change of government in 1997. It made the changes look like evolution rather than revolution!

❖ The second political advantage of this purchaser/provider split was that it distanced the Secretary of State from the decisions. When accused by an MP of letting his local acute services decline, the Secretary of State could respond, that it was not his responsibility and the MP should talk to the health authority. He might suggest that perhaps the consultants hadn't been pulling their weight; or perhaps the local GPs wanted to go elsewhere. Several Conservative MPs were able to debate and vote against the government on matters related to their hospital but the negative votes were kept to the immediate hospital and were never sufficient, with the opposition, to overthrow the government majority.

31

This device protected the government from a major debate on an issue of principle and avoided what would have been a substantial rebellion in their own ranks because of constituency interests. One of the reasons why I admire John Major is that he stuck firmly to the 1991 reforms even when his Government began to lose precious votes from its slim majority. The first time the general public became aware of this link, and the price John Major had paid, was with the closure of the A&E department at Barnet Hospital in the spring of 1997 when two Conservative MPs withdrew from the whip and for the period between March and May 1997 the Government was, technically, a minority Government.

What has been called the political rationale was the requirement to make the main policy initiative secret in order to ensure the reduction in the number of acute hospitals in the UK. The mechanism for doing it was the purchaser / provider split and the consequences for the Major Government in seeing it through were serious. Individual MPs withdrew support from their Party because they responded to the overwhelming public hostility to any change in the pattern of acute service provision. Unfortunately those who saw the effect of the policy on the distribution of acute hospitals became more cynical about politicians and political initiatives because of a lack of consistency between public announcements and events on the ground.

The attempt to rationalise acute hospital provision within a framework of fewer larger acute hospitals that could develop appropriate specialist services, was the last brave attempt to keep pace with clinical developments and to move away from the fundamental physical and geographical inequalities in the distribution of the acute hospital service that had more or less resisted attempts at reform for the first 45 years of the NHS. What has happened to this policy and to acute hospitals after the arrival of the Labour Government in 1997 is outlined below.

3 Acute Hospital Policy 1997 - 2003

The Labour Government's policy on the acute elective and specialist hospital services falls into two very distinct halves, 1997 – 1999 and 1999 and beyond, these equate almost exactly to the two secretaries of state, Frank Dobson and Alan Milburn. In 1997 Frank Dobson acquired an existing policy that was moving in a clear direction as explained above. Unfortunately for Dobson, the publicity surrounding cases like the Barnet A&E department, the greater willingness of the Colleges to publish their views about the future shape of the hospital service and the growing public awareness of a concerted rationalisation in acute hospitals made it more difficult for him to continue the policy at a time when the public were expecting great improvements in health from the first Labour Government in 18 years.

Dobson was unlucky in the hospital rationalisations that came his way. He had to approve the decision in East Kent with the rationalisation of acute services between Canterbury, Margate and Ashford and such was his and the Government's sensitivity to unpopularity that it was managed in a very indirect way. The reason why Canterbury had to lose its 24 hour core acute services was clear, open and well documented, but Dobson did not act for that reason. Instead he used the reason of the cervical screening errors to put across the closure as action to protect Canterbury women. The government 'spun' the publicity of that failure in clinical service, despite the fact that the issue should have been irrelevant to the grounds on which Canterbury lost its general acute hospital status.

By then there were doubts whether Dobson was prepared to see the rationalisation policy through. The answer came with the fluffed decision about the future of St. Bartholomew's Hospital in London. The decision was too near home for Dobson, he had to deal with some of the most politicised medical consultants in the business and in the end he backed off. The backing off at 'Barts' was to mark the end of the acute hospital rationalisation strategy introduced in 1991, although not the end of some of its objectives.

Dobson's policy problems were aggravated by the acute medical bed dilemma. There was a hidden weakness in the Conservative plan that had not been apparent in 1991, one that did not occur until the policy started to be successful. 24 hour acute hospitals with A&E departments, (and increasingly with medical admissions units), were being reduced in number and acutely ill medical patients were being directed to fewer hospitals. Acute medical bed numbers were falling nationally because hospitals retaining an acute medical admissions service were trying to do so with few if any additional beds to balance the closure of smaller acute units. As the policy rolled forward the problems for patients awaiting admission to an acute hospital bed highlighted this reduction in service quality and created public hostility. At this point it is necessary to pause in the narrative to update the reader on the generalist/specialist debate among the doctors.

The Intervention of the Doctors and New Labour's Response

Earlier in the chapter it was described how in 1996 the Royal College of Physicians of London had opted for the maintenance of general consultant physicians with a population base of 250,000, but that the Royal College of Surgeons of England had followed in 1997 with a plea for a population base of 450,000 to half a million in order to gather together all the main surgical specialties under one roof. The BMA was concerned at the major policy differences inherent in the two documents, both with respect to the size of acute hospitals required and their differing views on the future of the generalist consultant. The BMA played a brokering role in attempting to get the Colleges to agree on a single formula and a single strategy. The result was a publication, "Provision of Acute General Hospital Services : Consultation Document" produced by a Joint Working Party of the

BMA, the Royal College of Physicians of London and the Royal College of Surgeons of England in July 1998. The importance of this document can be easily missed because the bulk of it is a wish list relating to the number of consultants required in every hospital across a range of specialties and sub-specialties. However, if one reads it with the intention of discerning the future of the acute hospital, the nature of the agreement between the Colleges becomes clear.

The document sees the future acute hospital/acute medical centre as serving a population of nearly half a million. But it then goes on to indicate that the lack of sufficient acute medical beds in the current acute hospitals makes them increasingly unsuitable for future mergers of acute hospital services. The future is seen to lie with new build hospitals as the acute medical centres of the 21st century. These would contain an appropriate number of acute medical beds to meet the needs of a half million population. Some of these hospitals were claimed to exist. Many would have to be built, and the achievement of the long term goal was seen as taking potentially until 2020 or beyond as this new generation of hospitals was fully established. But what should be done in the meantime?

The document suggested bringing together two or more adjacent hospitals to create two distinct hospital services by gradually focussing the acute work in one hospital and all the specialist work in the other 'colder' less acute hospital. The term 'binary solution' best fits this concept although the phrase is not used in the document. At the time this document was written the NHS had examples of this formula evolving. One was from Wales in Swansea where the Morriston Hospital became the hot acute service and Singleton Hospital increasingly the colder specialist service. There were several other examples. This 'binary solution' was a way of keeping hold of sufficient acute medical beds to meet the anxieties of the RCP and to permit, for a while at least, the continuation of the generalist physician on acute medical take.

The Labour Government grabbed this option even more enthusiastically than the Conservatives adopted the clinical rationale of the medical Colleges in 1991; not least because it created an opportunity to veer away from the simple rationalisations that were the hallmark of 1991 to 1998. One of the reasons for this was a weakness of Labour's own making. They had abandoned the independence of purchasers and providers created in 1991 by changing the rhetoric, (health authorities and trusts not purchasers and providers, 'service agreements' not 'contracts'), but, crucially, they changed the power relationship by giving health authorities far greater control over trusts. (One aspect of this was the withdrawal of the trusts' freedom to decide their own consultant medical staffing which was given instead to Health Authorities.) They liked the 'binary solution' and the policy was adopted by Dobson. Its initial results included the merger of the Leeds hospitals into a single massive trust with a population base at least half as much again as the half million envisaged in the tripartite consultation document of July 1998.

With Alan Milburn's arrival, this 'binary solution' spread rapidly across UK cities, Glasgow, Newcastle, Manchester, Sheffield, Leicester and parts of London, and marked the start of the second phase of Labour's acute hospital initiatives. These cities witnessed trust mergers and the assumption that the 'binary solution' would lead to a differing status for individual hospitals. Some like Sheffield had already gone down that road with the transfer of A&E services to the Northern Hospital and others were still to plan their outcomes. Some of these 'binary solution' changes had occurred under the Conservatives between 1991 and 1997 such as Liverpool with the concentration of general acute services on the Royal Liverpool hospital. Others were being planned before 1997 because of major new hospital initiatives such as Edinburgh. What Labour did was to speed up dramatically the process by completing a series of mergers in cities where the hospitals' were relatively close together and where the city population might be more easily expected to identify with the solution.

None of this focus on the cities resolved the challenge of the counties. After the unpopularity of hard decisions such as East Kent the Labour Government has (with one exception) baulked at the challenge of building a suitable acute hospital service for the counties. Instead many remaining acute hospitals were gathered into a 'hub and spoke' relationship where they become feeder hospitals to the more specialist acute service in the cities. Basic generalist acute services are still provided in feeder/spoke hospitals and acute medical admission occurs via a linked A&E service but many specialist services were still provided only in the cities with teaching hospital provision; and everyone was required to travel or be transferred in an ambulance. This makes a nonsense of earlier targets to reduce inter-hospital transfers. This 'hub and spoke' model which is now reinforcing the mammoth city trusts goes right back to the inequality of geographical provision of health care that stuck fast in 1946 and which the Conservatives attempted to change in 1962 and1991 and Labour tried to change in 1977. It is rapidly undoing all the good that was achieved in the eight years after 1991 and is one explanation for the failure of the current acute hospital service policy to achieve an even distribution of high quality services.

There is also a weakness in New Labour's dealings with the traditional city based teaching hospitals. The teaching hospitals are always avid to secure the bulk of any new resources and to undertake additional clinical developments. They are the principal beneficiaries of the development of 'hub and spoke' policies and they realise that 'hub and spoke' will not only guarantee the continuing better resourcing of the teaching hospitals but will allow them to dictate the shape of clinical service development in exactly the same way as the Regional Health Authorities and the teaching hospitals treated the 'town' in the first 40 years of the NHS. These teaching institutions have clamoured for 'hub and spoke', whilst the 'spokes' have lacked organisational leadership and in particular have never been allowed to see clearly what the 1991 Strategy aimed to achieve for them.

'Hub' and 'spoke', the language of 1998/2000 has undergone several sophistications. Clinical care pathways involving 'fast tracking' patients to wherever the necessary specialist service is located sounds much better than 'hub' and 'spoke'. For most patients it means the same thing; those attending small to medium sized acute hospitals get fast-tracked to teaching hospitals, although outside the two chosen priorities of cancer and heart disease 'fast' is too optimistic a word; and those caught up in the wait for initial diagnostic support may prefer 'side-tracked'.

An alternative New Labour strategy for the counties has been to arrange patient flows so that for one range of clinical treatments the patient travels to hospital A and for another goes to hospital B, within the county. The double weakness of this is that all patients end up with more travelling over time, but the two hospitals do not get to develop, in county, the more specialist services for which the patient has still to travel out of county to obtain.

An example of what has to be achieved if the UK is to have an acceptable acute hospital service in the 21st century is provided by Stevenage and Welwyn Garden City in North Hertfordshire. The Lister Hospital in Stevenage supports a population of just below a quarter of a million and the Queen Elizabeth Hospital in Welwyn Garden City supports a population of just over a quarter million. They are 13 miles apart and joined by a motor-way. The only way that these communities can unite in support of a common clinical service of appropriate and higher quality is if an acute medical centre is built half way between the towns with adequate modern parking facilities. What this would do would be to give both communities a full modern acute medical and surgical service with all the main surgical specialties on site and the opportunity for a number of tertiary specialist services to be developed as well. That was the 1991 Strategy; that was the way it was going. Now they have been 'hubbed and spoked' to be drawn yet again into London where the distance between North Hertfordshire and the city of London will continue to mark them as second class citizens in the NHS.

Finally, in February 2003 the government released its new guidance on reconfiguring hospital services. It backs off all reconfiguration unless there is public approval locally, which means little or no future rationalisations. The government has surrendered to the view supported by Dr Taylor, the retired physician who took a Labour seat in 2001 campaigning to restore and retain acute services in Kidderminster Hospital. This abandonment of progress towards clinically safer, higher quality, larger acute hospitals gives some short term popularity, but is no response to the challenge of maintaining a modern public health care system. History will come to record this action as the point at which Labour lost the 'New NHS'.

New Labour's Response to PFI

The most controversial aspect of Labour's failure in creating a viable acute hospital service concerns the Private Finance Initiative (PFI). PFI was a Conservative government initiative that has been enthusiastically championed and extended by the current Labour Government. The idea was faulty in conception, it has now been proved to have serious disadvantages in terms of the present and future quality and delivery of health care and its present extension will only add to the future problems of the UK health care system and highlight the failure of the NHS.

Why use PFI? One argument is that it is quicker to get new modern hospitals built and available for patients who would wait longer for public sector capital resources to be made available. Yet if we look at the history of the NHS over the last 40 years since Enoch Powell initiated the DGH's, the PFI contribution in the last few years does not stand out as a period of tremendous growth. Rather, the schemes have dragged, some have been unable to go ahead and the first two full hospitals to be successfully opened have had to start a programme of immediate supplementary building.

It is claimed that PFI has a tight set of financial requirements that ensure that there is a cost benefit from using the private sector in terms of a quicker hospital build, and in the subsequent revenue benefits of running it. There is a formula for 'proving' this cost benefit before a PFI scheme is signed off. The first two completed hospital schemes in Carlisle and Norwich were signed off as meeting these financial criteria on the assumption of a given number of acute medical beds. Both hospital trusts now realise that they need additional acute medical beds and these are now being built. It is questionable whether the schemes would have been originally signed off if based on the genuine number of acute medical beds required; or had the quality of the buildings been properly specified.

Another PFI example is the turnkey radiology department at Wellhouse Trust in south London. Clinicians had too little input and were built a box that already does not have the capacity to be equipped as a modern up to date radiology service with equipment in sufficient quantity across the different radiology modalities. Both this and the examples above are illustrations of squeezing the hospital and its facilities to fit into the financial requirements for PFI approval instead of tailoring the hospital to meet and provide for the needs of a 21st century health care system.

Concerns have already been expressed about the durability of the new PFI hospitals implying that they have been built primarily for the 30 year period of the contract rather than for a longer life. There is no data in the public domain at the moment as to whether and to what extent this is true. The chief fear must be that at least the first generation of PFIs will face immediate and intractable problems in providing for the health care needs of the populations assigned to them and these in turn will led to expensive ad hoc modifications and extensions that will characterise the failed approach of the present NHS.

The Government has now launched a new PFI hospital programme for 100 new hospitals by 2010 with financial assistance to all tenderers to encourage response. The private sector will cherry pick; there is no indication that the problems of first wave PFIs will be addressed; the volume and timescales are clearly too ambitious; ("but at least we had the vision even though we didn't reach the target" – it becomes so easy to write the spin!) One leading private contractor has already pulled out because the bureaucracy is too costly. Finally there will be a small number of Treasury build hospitals; so some traditional Labour strongholds might get a good deal!

The case for and against PFI justifies a much more in-depth study than this brief critical summary here. It is not a mechanism with any vision of quality health care; it is easier to undertake in some parts of the country than others, which will reinforce all the inequalities of current hospital provision and it will take so long to complete that other pressures will have overcome Labour's acute hospital policy before the hospitals are ever in place.

4 Elective Surgery and Day Case Surgery

The general analysis of acute hospital provision above applies equally to acute surgical services and there have been many references in the text to acute surgery. However, there is an important issue, not yet considered, that has a significant influence upon the size and location of hospital services, namely day case surgery.

One of the issues that is crucial to the future success of a health care system in the UK is day case surgery. All elective surgery falls into one of four categories.

- Very minor surgery such as skin lesions that GPs are still willing to carry out in GP practices.

- Relatively minor surgery carried out by hospital doctors (and now occasionally by separately trained nurses) in outpatient clinics and treatment rooms of the 'lumps and bumps' variety and including some of the high volume of endoscopies, skin lesions etc. now undertaken in hospital settings.

- A much wider range of minor and intermediate surgical procedures carried out in separately established day case units that might either be within the main acute hospital, or in the grounds as a self standing surgical unit, or even at an independent site away from the acute hospital. A few GP clinics have established a full theatre, anaesthetic room and treatment room to locate some of this day surgery in their practice.

- The complex and some of the less complex surgery that is undertaken on patients in acute/elective hospitals who are inpatients even if they only stay over for one night.

Some NHS trusts have linked the last two of these levels more formally by leaving open one elective surgical inpatient bed until 10pm at night, to allow for the possibility of a day case surgery patient suddenly needing to remain in hospital overnight. This capacity helps to broaden the scope of work that is undertaken in day case units.

Headline figures suggest that in the USA 80% of all elective surgery is undertaken as day case, so avoiding the need for an inpatient bed: in the UK the proportion is below 50%. It is impossible to compare the figures exactly because any trust or group of surgeons wishing their day case figures to look better are able to transfer into day case theatres types of cases that their colleagues would do in outpatient clinics and treatment rooms. A wide variety of endoscopies is performed by surgeons and sometimes by physicians in theatres and different definitions of theatre and non-theatre work between trusts and even between individual surgeons makes tight comparison impossible. Nevertheless, after an enthusiastic start on the development of day surgery nearly twenty years ago, the UK has lagged behind the day case proportions achieved in the wider English speaking world. Annual studies undertaken by the British Association of Day Surgery show just how variable is the attitude towards, and the volume of work undertaken, on a day case surgical basis. Some NHS trusts seem to take pride in volumes of day case surgery below 20%.

There is no doubt, however, that the capacity exists, (from good practice that is already being achieved in the UK), to allow 70% of all elective surgery (on a standard definition) to be achieved on a day case basis. Had this happened throughout the UK a not insignificant proportion of elective surgical beds could have been made available to meet the growing demand for acute medical beds. The reasons for this are listed below and they are partly reinforced by current government policy.

- There is a legitimate policy debate about what constitutes quality in elective surgery. Those in favour of day case surgery point to the benefit to the patient in committing only one day for the procedure; in starting early into post surgical rehabilitation; in the not insignificant advantage of reducing the risk of hospital acquired infections and in having the opportunity to rehabilitate more effectively as well as more quickly in the familiar setting of the home. Today's day surgical patients have 24 hour contact numbers during their period of rehabilitation and as indicated above many day case units have the fall back of an inpatient bed should any outcome be questionable.

There is an alternative quality argument that focuses upon the value of convalescence in a safer hospital setting (although that would not apply to all wards), the benefits for some patients who have wholly inappropriate home facilities and the fact that if something goes suddenly wrong the patient is nearer to appropriate hospital staff. Inevitably each surgeon has to weigh the quality considerations alongside the cost and throughput implications of having a high proportion of work as *inpatient* elective surgery.

- There has always been a resistance by a proportion of consultants to undertaking sessions in day case units, particularly when they are not on the main hospital site. Many surgeons believe that they should not be wasting their time on a full list of only minor and intermediate cases. This argument is, to say the least, disingenuous because most surgeons across the specialties could choose to be more ambitious in the cases they allocate to day case surgery – in the interests of their patients for the quality reasons given above. Those consultants that try to avoid more than a minor commitment to day case surgery will often hand over a list to a non-consultant staff grade surgeon or to a trainee surgeon guaranteeing a much more modest ambition for day case surgery.

The government's latest initiative is encouraging and funding diagnostic and treatment centres including day case surgery in stand alone units mainly away from the major acute hospital sites. This is in direct response to existing consultant surgeon resistance. It involves importing labour, both nurses and non-consultant career grade doctors, and sadly reinforces the idea that day case surgery is low level, lower complexity work that will not help win hearts and minds for a wide acceptance of day case surgery among the generalists of consultant surgeons. Even worse these new 'centres', (perhaps peripheries would be better), risk being isolated from the main acute hospital with a lack of inter-action leading to error leading to . . . "I told you so" . . . responses. By going down this road the government seriously risks *damaging* UK achievement in day case surgery, not enhancing it.

- It is important not to *over* state this last point, for the system is sometimes undermined by surgeons themselves for reasons that are not creditable. Day case lists can deliberately be filled up by very minor work so that the consultant need never attend. This can be done by transferring work out of treatment rooms and outpatient clinics and putting it into day case theatres to give a false impression of activity.

- Although evidence is not yet available there is a very real concern that the government's commitment to using the private sector and non-UK hospitals for elective surgery to reduce the waiting list could have a perverse effect. There is no question that the private hospital, case for case, would prefer this to be done on an inpatient rather than a day case basis. It ensures that their beds get used more regularly and the cost for a room can often give a greater certainty of profit than the tightly priced surgical procedure. It is up to the surgeons whether those patients transferred to the private sector will or will not be regarded as day case. The surgeons also face the problem of double standards. If a particular type of case is always undertaken by a surgeon who works privately on a day case basis why is that surgeon not working on a day case basis within the NHS? There is a litany of ingenious answers to this question the most common of which is that, "...I encourage my more straight-forward cases to go privately so that my more complex cases can have an inpatient NHS bed".

- There is a growing commitment to laparoscopic/minimal access surgery that reduces the severity of the surgery for the patient and substantially improves rehabilitation speeds. As this trend continues it should be making its contribution to the growth of the proportion of all elective surgery that is done as a day case. There is at present no significant evidence to suggest that this is taking place and one of the issues is that the type of theatre used for surgery often dictates whether the patient will be inpatient or day case because theatres lack sufficient flexibility.

- Finally, returning to the annual research undertaken by the British Association of Day Case Surgery, there would appear to be a growing transfer from treatment room and outpatient clinic to day case theatre as day case theatre capacity has increased. This is quite clearly not the purpose of increasing the day case theatre capacity and this drift has not been policed.

45

There was no major government initiative or statement of support for day case surgery after 1997 until, in 2002, the Government appointed a surgeon to oversee and proselytise, though with no available sanctions. Meanwhile those within the NHS would have to admit that the enthusiasm of the early campaigners for day case surgery is now sadly missing in many hospitals. As day case capacity rolls marginally forward too much of it is merely being mis-used as indicated above. Even the national statistics showing some UK day case growth year on year should be interpreted with great caution because of the increasing volume of work that is not appropriate for inclusion. Diagnostic and Treatment Centres are a response, but there are real dangers of isolation, of quality control and of ensuring appropriate standards. They represent New Labour's 'go it alone' strategy, which can so often mean lack of integration with consultants and services within the acute hospital.

5 Conclusion

In judging the appropriateness and suitability of acute hospital service provision in the UK two questions dominate.

- Is the service provided, by range and quality, achieving outcomes appropriate to a first world country at the beginning of the 21st century?

- Do all the public have equal and timely access to that service on the basis of need?

No-one disputes that it is impossible to give an unqualified 'yes' to either question and the acute hospital service debate therefore focuses upon the hospital provision strategy necessary to achieve these goals. It has been argued in this chapter that at least two initiatives are required.

- The Medical Royal Colleges of Surgeons and Physicians and the BMA summarised in 1998 why an *acute* hospital service required to be organised around a 450,000 to half million population and why a single major *acute* medical service site offered the best opportunity to achieve quality outcomes; when this could be supported by an adequate number of acute medical and surgical beds on site.

- 60 years of inequality of access by distance and major variability in quality standards have to be ended by measures far more radical and far more politically robust that anything yet attempted. Failure to tackle inequality in a population deliberately sensitised to this issue by the constant publication of performance data and by the promises of this Labour government is one of the biggest ever politically generated threats to the future of our State funded system.

As argued in the chapter the present government's policy and funding initiatives, on balance, appear unlikely to succeed. The points below summarise the reasons discussed.

i The PFI strategy is misconceived; it cannot achieve an appropriate geographical balance of hospital provision: it cannot achieve it in the timescale envisaged; the 30 year rule is a major threat to the physical quality of the facilities; the financial rules are still too tight to allow full necessary provision for the population served and we are building ad hoc without a thought through national strategy for acute hospital provision. The poor public sector record on capital build and the power of over-mighty public sector unions should be tackled in their own right and not by the back door of PFI.

ii Acute and elective surgical bed planning needs a clear national decision between government and professions on the role of day surgery and the framework within which it will have to be achieved. Without it acute hospital bed numbers will be guesswork. The government has not addressed this issue seriously and the use of the private sector for elective surgery has muddied the waters and made clear national standards less likely.

iii The government has finally backed away from acute hospital site rationalisations in the face of public hostility. The 'binary solution' in the cities shows very little progress towards site rationalisation and the evidence of 'hub' and 'spoke'; clinical care pathways and joint hospital networks give more the appearance of accepting inadequate hospital provision and simply trying to make it work better. If one tracks individual clinical pathways the totality of pathways often cover a region rather than being confined to a more specific locality and as such returns to the two tier health care of the past.

iv There is no sign that the Government (or the Opposition) are prepared to risk opening the political debate about trading distance from hospital for higher quality 21st century clinical outcomes. Indeed, a policy in which the public decide the hospital configurations due to patient empowerment seems guaranteed to have the present pattern of acute hospital provision 'set in aspic'.

The great risk for the Labour government is that the new National *Health* Service will fail totally, despite its new funding level. If its relatively poorer international outcomes lead many in the top quartile of incomes to desert it for private consultation, diagnostic support and elective surgery, the looming labour supply crisis will cause a collapse of standards in the public sector. (See the next chapter). To provide a *hospital* service to meet modern clinical standards is *essential* to avoid this, and within that acute provision high quality diagnostic services by access and quality, and good elective surgical access and outcomes are as important as A&E and acute medical provision. Indeed to prevent the collapse of public provision one could almost argue that the former is more important that the latter.

If the public cannot be persuaded to trade distance for quality, and if a national NHS hospital provision plan is not achieved soon, full national and equally accessible public provision of healthcare will fail. With its policy on hospital reconfigurations New Labour appears to have opted out of any attempt to lead the NHS towards its only likely route to success.

CHAPTER 3

STAFFING A NATIONAL HEALTH SERVICE

1 Introduction

This chapter considers the labour supply deficit in the NHS and assesses the likelihood of current initiatives overcoming the deficit. It deals with each major profession in turn and in each considers the options for labour substitution. Where the labour supply deficit is modest and/or where there is no threat to the maintenance of NHS services the chapter acknowledges this without further analysis.

The chapter concentrates first on the crucial issue of medical labour supply. But the choice must not cause misunderstanding. The substitution of doctors by nurses, radiographers and other professional staff after specialist training for specific tasks has developed and will grow. Doctors alone cannot now work effectively without nurses and a whole range of professions allied to medicine. The failure of nursing supply on its own would be catastrophic and would change the whole nature of health delivery. Chapter 4 will illustrate how even the failure of support staff supply is radically changing social care for the elderly. Despite all this, securing medical supply remains the most crucial of all the many labour supply challenges faced by the government.

2 The Shortage of Doctors

Background

There is a historical background that explains certain tensions and 'no go areas' in the medical supply debate which are not understandable without that background. To avoid the lengthy insertion of a condensed history of UK medicine into the chapter, the bullet points focus upon the issues relevant to the analysis and are not historically comprehensive. Changes to this background after 1993 will be analysed in the later text.

- ### Consultants and GPs
  The two main branches of medicine are general practice in primary care, (the GP); and hospital practice, the latter divided initially between trainees (the junior doctors) and consultants. To complicate the picture those who become GPs spend part of their training in hospitals and are therefore, statistically, included in the broad title of junior doctors. Originally GPs trained in hospitals and after attaining a certain level of experience could apply to enter general practice as a GP. This meant flexibility in the labour market when the availability of hospital consultant and GP posts fluctuated. Subsequently a GP training scheme was introduced which took junior doctors, at a certain stage, into community based GP training, one consequence of which was to reduce the flexibility to switch between the two branches of the profession. The main purpose of this change; to increase the quality of training of newly appointed GPs, was, however, both laudable and necessary. Today there are roughly three GPs for every two hospital consultants.

- ### Non-Consultant Career Grades
  In addition to consultants and trainee doctors in hospitals there has been a small, but now rapidly growing category of *career* grade

doctors who are not consultants. These are doctors whose current range and balance of training are insufficient for them to become consultants. Nevertheless they are able to practice medicine within the framework of their individual capabilities, depending upon how extensive was their previous medical training, and these boundaries have to be set by the appropriate hospital consultants. Until recently, the title of the largest group of such doctors was 'staff grade'. Staff grades were introduced in 1988 to achieve a better balance of career grade doctors to trainee doctors in hospitals and their numbers were initially limited to a maximum of 10% of consultant numbers, specialty by specialty. Now there is no limit and today the three groups of hospital staff divide roughly between 35% consultants, 10% non-consultant career grades and 55% trainees.

- **Junior Hospital Doctors**
  For many years trainee hospital doctors went through a lengthy training scheme across several increasingly senior grades. They started as pre-registration house officers and, usually after a year, they registered to become senior house officers (SHOs). After completing the necessary SHO training they could apply to become registrars in a given specialty by competitive interview and, for most, progress was determined by the prevailing balance of registrar posts and trained SHOs; hence two or more years were spent at this level. After suitable training they applied for senior registrar posts, again by competitive interview and some trainees stuck at this level without further progress if the supply of posts was inadequate; eventually choosing to go off and do something else. Senior registrars could, after suitable training, apply for consultant posts and again the length of time in training varied according to supply and demand. Some could spend twenty years going from pre-registration house officer to becoming a consultant, some could get there in ten years.

- **International Variations in Medical Training**

  This primarily 'practice based' training system was copied in the old Commonwealth Dominions and in the USA. Some or many of its characteristics were copied in other Commonwealth countries. Across the world, however, medical training varies enormously. In several Mediterranean countries medical qualification is achieved academically and the practice of medicine begins largely after qualifying. Several countries in Eastern Europe train within very narrow specialisms e.g. nine separate divisions of radiology in Russia with doctors often not trained outside one modality. There are many such variations well established within the culture of their own national health care system. The medical profession in the UK is proud of its success in delivering competent practicing consultants on the day of appointment and strives to retain this characteristic of British medicine. This is the chief reason why the UK medical profession is anxious about any large scale, international, importation of career grade doctors unable to practice at consultant level.

- **Overseas Trainees**

  In the first period of the NHS trainee doctors from abroad, largely new Commonwealth countries, came to the UK to train. In the main they returned to their own country to practice high quality medicine and to disseminate good practice. The advantage was reciprocal; the UK received a steady flow of trainees; the country of origin received trained doctors funded in the UK and taught to high standards. In more recent decades the demand for consultants, and the income opportunities in the UK, led more such trainees to stay here as consultants, diminishing the reciprocal benefit to the new Commonwealth.

- **Working Hours**

  One of the traditional characteristics of UK hospital medicine was that consultants worked in the daytime Monday to Friday and were

54

on call from home on a rota during the evenings and weekends. For some the rota could be one in two and the onerousness depended upon the specialty and the size of hospital teams. At weekends and in the evenings trainee doctors worked in the hospital or were on call in the hospital. This was when senior registrars finally learnt how to run a hospital specialty service, but with the back up of the on-call consultant. Inevitably trainee doctors worked many hours and as the work in these hours became more pressured junior doctors leaders campaigned for and achieved a growing number of controls which reduced the extent of this commitment, below 96 hours per week and gradually to 72 hours. This has been achieved by a 'New Deal' agreement which sought to increase shift and partial shift working and to reduce the traditional on-call to 72 hours. Audit Commission data shows many hospitals are not compliant with these targets and the south of England and Wales are the furthest from target, ranging between 20% and 41% compliance. The European Working Time Directive applies to trainee doctors and its further restrictions on working time are developed later in this chapter.

- **Medical Contracts**
One often misunderstood feature of UK medical employment concerns the nature of doctors' contracts. In general practice doctors were self employed contractors required to provide particular services to their patients, with optional extras, and paid largely according to the size of their patient list. Over time the tasks and the payments became more complex and work related. Now, after some experimentation with salaried employment GPs are being offered a salaried contract making them employees of the NHS and directly managed through the PCTs, which in turn they have, collectively, an important say in managing.

Hospital consultants were always salaried, but with a difference. They alone in hospital medicine were responsible for their own medical indemnity insurance. This meant that an action for negligence was an action against a doctor not against the hospital. Thus the consultant had some real control over what medical work could and could not be done. The ending of this responsibility, at the request of the profession due to mounting costs, marked the beginning of a very significant change in the relationship between the hospital trust and the consultant, but one which has only really become apparent with the advent of a generation of consultants that never experienced this responsibility for indemnity insurance.

The contractual position on consultants private practice has always been the stuff of legend and make-believe. The reality was always more prosaic. *Any* consultant could do private practice up to 10% of NHS salary, but if over three years this was exceeded, the consultant was *required* to take a maximum part-time contract losing one eleventh of NHS salary with no diminution of NHS workload. This contract further stated that the consultant had to commit "…substantially the whole of his time," to NHS work. This formula has many interpretations and at local level has always been applied according to local practice. If such a consultant was conscientious with NHS work, did the whole of his ten session commitment properly, but was a workaholic who spent all his free (non-sleeping) time in the private sector, was he in breach of the rule? Widely across the NHS the answer was negative; if he chose this lifestyle there was no breach of NHS contract. The fact that some consultants, over the years, have been found to have skipped some of their NHS commitments was always a separate, disciplinary, issue not to be confused with the proper interpretation of the contract. A final point on private practice is that it is not equally available across the medical specialties. Crudely, the surgical half of hospital medicine (surgeons, gynaecologists, anaesthetists, radiologists, histopathologists) can in the main choose to access private practice and many do so. For the medical half of hospital medicine (physicians, psychiatrists, pathologists in most sub specialties, A&E medicine) private practice is somewhat more difficult to find. The exceptions in some sub-specialties do not undermine this division of the profession although the split between acute and elective work across the medical profession is also a key factor. What is important is that hospital consultants are divided between those who do and those who do not have reasonable access to choice about private work, and this can shape the way in which the whole UK profession responds to change and to challenges.

Recent changes in post-graduate medical training 1993-1997

The significance of 1993 is that it is the date when the Calman Report on medical training began to be implemented.

The Calman Committee merged the registrar and senior registrar training posts into a single new grade of Specialist Registrar (SpR) and limited the period of training required of an SpR to either 4,5 or 6 years according to specialty. At the end of this period, subject to satisfactory progression in acquiring clinical skills, trainees obtained a (new) certificate of competence in specialist training (CCST) and were eligible to be appointed as consultants. *And at the same time they lost their right to continue in training for longer than a maximum one year extension.* For the first time ever trainees fell off a conveyor belt whether or not they had secured a consultant post, in order that the supply of training posts year on year would not dry up, as had happened previously. This was because senior registrar posts became blocked when trained senior registrars could not find consultant posts.

The move was very radical in that it secured a permanent flow of trainees going through the system and without this reform medical supply today would be even worse than the present near catastrophe. Future historians of the NHS will come to see Calman and his team, as having saved the NHS from a major medical supply collapse by the end of the 1990s. This availability of the Calman trainees in the nick of time should not be underestimated. The Royal College of Anaesthetists originally introduced only a four year period of training at SpR level and this enabled it to deliver an unprecedented number of CCST holders (over 1,300) over a three year period – and at the end of those three years there was still a shortage of applicants for consultant anaesthetist posts! In mental health, in many branches of surgery, in a few branches of medicine like gastroenterology and in the diagnostic services of radiology and histopathology, the increase in the supply of trained applicants for consultant posts could not keep pace with demand, despite the Calman surge in supply. The hard figures of growing demand in the mid to late 1990s fully justify the importance given here to the conveyor belt as the lifeline that avoided a complete supply failure. In the three years from 1994 to 1997 hospital consultant medical staffing rose at a yearly average of 6.34% against a requirement in the Calman Report that government must guarantee a minimum of 5% a year compound growth until at least the year 2000/01. At no previous time in the history of the NHS had any government funded this amount of growth over this period of time.

So where did this growth in demand come from? It was a compound of many issues and pressures. Controlling the hours of medical trainees increased the pressure. The growing switch from generalist to specialist hospital medical services played an important part and that in turn was spurred on by the growing outcomes debate caused by e.g., the CEPOD Reports already quoted in Chapter 2. Interestingly, this demand was not evenly balanced between the medical specialties with the result that for the first time in history of the NHS the growth of hospital medical staffing was no longer 'balanced' across different medical specialties. Surgery, anaesthetics, mental health, radiology, radiotherapy, histopathology and some physician specialties did very well. Most of medicine experienced a slower growth whilst the lack of commitment to community medicine virtually wiped out the specialty; chemical pathology experienced a major decline and growth was virtually eliminated from obstetrics. The consequence of this was that the focus of expansion was based upon servicing waiting lists and the balance of total medical resources was redistributed.

Consultant Expansion After 1997

The change of government in May 1997 introduced a significant check to the consultant expansion described above. The Labour Party has been traditionally more hostile in its dealings with hospital consultants. There was an instinctive dislike of the perceived elistism of hospital consultants and strong opposition to the whole concept of private practice. A new government with a landslide majority felt empowered to 'tackle' the hospital consultants and the broad agenda from the start has been to establish their status as simply employees, who should work fixed hours; should be team players rather than always team leaders and who should be firmly weaned off private practice in the short and medium term.

Despite this agenda Labour has always had its supporters among hospital consultants, but these came almost wholly from what was earlier described as 'the medical half' of the hospital consultant body. In 1997 a wider body of doctors hoped for faster growth from New Labour, but in the last five years this support among hospital consultants has diminished quite rapidly.

The effect of new government policy on consultant staffing was almost instantaneous. Between 1997 and 1999 the annual rate of growth in hospital consultant WTEs fell to 4.35% per annum. This was a one third reduction from the previous three year period and, significantly, it took consultant growth below the crucial 5% a year minimum growth necessary if the Calman training reforms were to succeed.

The way this was done was quite simple. The government withdrew from hospital trusts the freedom to make their own consultant appointments as they thought fit. From 1997 *all* hospital consultant posts, even ordinary replacements, had to be approved by the Health Authority. Control passed back up the chain of command. At the same time government introduced its health priorities in cancer, heart disease, mental health and subsequently elderly medicine. The chosen specialties were encouraged to grow whilst high demand specialties like orthopaedics and ophthalmology were no longer prioritised for growth. In reality some strong teaching hospitals got the Health Authority to rubber stamp most of their decisions, but for the generality of hospital trusts the effect of the new controls and priorities was immediate.

What the government failed to appreciate in 1997 was that medical supply was far too complex to be *significantly* rebalanced between specialties in the short term. All that happened was that they failed to achieve growth targets in their priority specialties because there were not enough trainees nearing completion of training, but they *did* achieve a slowdown, sometimes significant, in the non-priority specialties. The net result was the collapse of consultant expansion to below the Calman minimum of 5% per annum referred to above. By 1999 the supply/demand deficit had clearly worsened and there was added confusion within the hospital training structure that requires explanation.

When the Calman training reforms were introduced the Regional Postgraduate Deans were given control of the number of SpR posts in each Region. The theory was that the Deans could increase or decrease this number so that over the four to six years of SpR training the supply of CCST holders (trained doctors ready for consultant posts) would be sufficient for demand. The fall in the consultant growth rate in non-priority specialties thus affected SpR posts at the front end i.e. by cuts in years one and two of SpR training and this in turn caused a build up of trained SHOs unable to access SpR posts. In some medical specialties there were SHOs stuck for six years by 2001, because they were determined about their choice of specialty and stayed doggedly in the queue. Subsequently government has taken control away from the Deans and transferred it to a national agency for easier control of training, but this of itself, does not remove the problem. Rapid changes in medical priorities upset labour supply if they ignore the lead time necessary to re-balance the training structure. Labour were in far too much of a hurry and surprisingly had not learnt the mechanics of medical training whilst in opposition.

To reinforce the importance of these 'mechanics' let us take the case of a priority specialty where government wants to *increase* the number of consultants and *increase* the number of SpR posts. Consultants in the main divide their NHS time between clinical work, audit and teaching/training. (The emphasis on audit has been growing for the last ten years, is a current government priority, and the 5% - 10% of consultant time it takes is not reducible.) Demand for clinical work is growing and government priorities are speeding up the growth. Virtually all hospitals recognised as training centres by the medical specialty concerned are slightly over, at, or slightly below the maximum number of SpRs that can be properly trained with the consultant time available. Any increase in SpR numbers would be in years one and then two with higher supervision needs, and if an increase in SpRs occurred it could only mean poorer training quality or reduced consultant clinical workload. Only as consultant numbers grow can safe trainee expansion occur. Reducing consultant supervision of trainees, or recognising all hospitals as SpR teaching establishments will reduce the training quality, but the government's stress on greater *clinical service* productivity threatens to produce just this outcome. The result has been that even in priority specialties trainee growth has not, and cannot, happen at more than a moderate pace and even so is raising anxieties about training quality in several specialties.

By tackling this problem from a position of knowledge and understanding Calman and his colleagues introduced the 1993 radical reforms to enable the system to increase supply by somewhat over 5% per annum as long as government funded the growth. The system worked, but when Calman as CMO tried to teach Milburn the realities of medical supply, the message must have been unpopular; Calman went and when the current CMO Donaldson was appointed, Milburn stripped the post of its responsibility for medical staffing and gave it to a new control structure closer to himself – or at least more influenceable by himself.

The National Plan and Beyond: the unfolding of the medical supply crisis

One thousand new medical undergraduate places... Dobson, the Secretary of State, announced as a new initiative in July 1997. It was/is absolutely essential and its greater emphasis upon GP undergraduate training is also very necessary. But this required time; to establish new university capacity and to staff it appropriately. By October 2001 only 350 of these places were occupied by an undergraduate. Even so this development was a necessary foundation for the National Plan.

The National Plan of 1999 announced 7,500 new consultants by 2004, but target dates are now slipping beyond the next general election. Not surprisingly 'The National Plan' is not now a phrase in Ministerial pronouncements as other health initiatives crowd in to take the headlines. This last part of the medical section of the chapter will argue that a series of factors have de-stabilised the drive for more consultants and that as the awful reality begins to dawn on the government, the very latest policy initiatives show increasing desperation. These 'events' are dealt with separately below, not always in chronological order; between them they paint a grim picture for any government.

• The Cancer Initiative

Cancer is taken as an illustration of what can go wrong even within priority services on which the government has staked its reputation. With great publicity Professor Mike Richards was appointed as 'Cancer Czar'. He was asked to identify how quickly medical staffing could be increased in six key medical specialties (but excluding surgery). Professor Richards undertook a proper and meticulous survey. He added up all the trainees going through the hospital system, assumed that none of them would stall at any point in their career progression, assumed that they would not take a year off after completing their training, assumed that every trainee would take a full time post as a consultant immediately on qualifying. This produced a maximum figure of 971 consultants that could be added to the labour force by 2004 across the six specialties, as a ceiling figure with caveats relating to all the points listed above.

The Prime Minister (not Professor Richards) personally chose to announce a major new government initiative to appoint a thousand extra cancer consultants, ('a thousand' sounds so much better than '971'). There was never any chance of achieving 971 let alone 1,000 because inevitably some doctors will be delayed going through training, many more will take a year off, many will choose to have part time and not full time jobs and some will go and work elsewhere. (It is interesting to note that in answers to parliamentary questions the Department of Health stuck firmly to the number 971 and there is no more mention of a thousand.) No longer will this number of appointments be achieved by 2004, instead the target date is slipping because one by one each caveat above is having a negative impact, despite some importation. If it takes to 2006 to achieve 971 this will actually be below the 6.42% compound growth in annual consultant numbers that was being achieved between 1994 and 1997.

In fact the outcome for the government may be much worse. Several of these six specialties like radiology and radiotherapy are professions where the proportion of woman doctors is rising rapidly, now over 50% of all newly appointed consultants. Women are more likely to work part-time and to take time away for families. Several of these specialties like radiology and histopathology are clearly experiencing an extreme deficit of supply, probably now one quarter of total NHS radiology demand cannot be filled at consultant level. In one six month period in 1998 there were as many radiology consultant vacancies advertised as in *all* medical specialties taken together excluding only cardiology. Radiology is witnessing real growth (5% to 10% annually) in the number of genuinely part-time consultants (ie those opting for fewer than 10 sessions a week), finding employment on their own terms; perhaps to use more time for private practice. These trends are all leaching away the carefully planned national supply statistics.

- **The EU Working Time Directive**
  The government decision to accept a fixed timetable for the introduction and application of the EU Working Time Directive for trainee doctors creates significant problems for the UK despite the longer timescale for compliance by August 1st 2004. EU countries have very different systems for training doctors. The UK has traditionally required trainee doctors to acquire considerable practical experience before being eligible for a consultant post in order to guarantee the maintenance of consultant quality. This is not universal in the EU and some countries require their doctors to gain their principal experience whilst practicing as a qualified specialist. For the latter countries it is easier to adapt to the Working Time directive than for the UK. Because of these differences in training and philosophy the Working Time Directive is almost uniquely disadvantageous to the UK within the EU.

Much junior medical time was spent on duty in the hospital at nights and weekends either working or 'sleeping-in' on a hospital on-call rota that could be quite arduous. But to get guided supervision working alongside and being taught by a consultant required a serious daytime commitment. This is why hours of work could be over 72 or even 96 hours a week. Calman training reduced the number of years a doctor spent in hospital training, so that maintaining the best quality training hours was essential. UK based initiatives to increase shift and partial shift working and reduce the on-call commitment in the 'New Deal' agreement had been making progress for a decade. Now, the EU directive with its 58 maximum weekly hours and no duty period in excess of 13 hours has undermined the less ambitious voluntary progress of the last decade and makes the calls on the trainee staff, in most specialties, a contractual impossibility if they are also to work alongside consultants during the day. In October 2000 the European Court of Justice stipulated that if a trainee is available in the hospital it must count as duty, even if the trainee is sleeping. If implemented in August 2004 this additional condition would ensure the immediate breakdown of night time *medical* cover in a swathe of smaller to medium sized acute hospitals. The government's position is on a knife edge and August 2004 must be one of the prime dates for the visible collapse of the 'New NHS'.

When the UK's own shift and partial shift initiatives were underway in the 1990s there were two national initiatives that affected this debate.

i The CEPOD Report, 'Who Operates When', referred to in Chapter 2, argued for a *consultant* presence at night to do the *genuinely* emergency work that could not be left until the following day, with consultants sleeping in if necessary. One great advantage of this, the real thrust of the CEPOD Report, was to improve the quality of clinical outcomes. Its by-product would be to allow trainees to protect their daytime hours for more focused and productive training. But one inevitable consequence is that it *reduces* consultant clinical productivity as far as the routine clinical work of the specialty is concerned and therefore aggravates the medical supply shortage at consultant level, with a threatened adverse affect on waiting lists.

ii The second initiative concerned the staff grade doctor. In October 1997 a new staff grade contract was signed with the BMA which abolished numerical restrictions on staff grade numbers, which made them free to be employed at any time of the day or night and which offered significant potential enhancements in salary for unsocial hours. Today staff grade (now non-consultant career grade) involves a significant number of non-UK doctors from third world countries whose training has been insufficient to qualify them as a CCST holding applicant for a consultant post.

The BMA had wanted to avoid sleeping in commitments for consultants in the future and its contract for 'career grades', ensured that the balance of night-time and weekend support could be provided by relatively well paid (due to unsocial hours) career grades when trainee doctors were not available. This method of using career grades does not focus upon high productivity; but it gives medical cover and minimises pressure on consultants to 'sleep in'.

These methodologies for covering trainee doctor absence from night-time and weekend cover had been identified before 1997. The problem for the government is that these solutions cut overall consultant clinical productivity. By committing the UK to target dates for implementing the full EU Directive for trainee doctors the process of change is speeded up and, if implemented, will sharpen the fall in productivity and increase the medical supply side deficit.

- **Specialists v Generalists in Hospital Medicine**

The previous chapter referred to the gradual decline in the proportion of consultants who were general surgeons or general physicians and the rise in direct appointments to consultant sub-specialties. This long term trend is developing rapidly in surgery but is more limited in medicine because the Royal College of Physicians still supports general medical take, i.e., consultant physicians on-call at night being regarded as competent to respond to all acute medical admissions. Even here, however, there is evidence that the Royal College of Physicians is re-thinking this commitment in a way that would align more to the position of the Royal College of Surgeons. The Physicians are now committed to training specialist physicians in acute medicine who might eventually replace medical take, with 24 hour cover from consultants in 'acute medicine'. This trend from generalist to specialist in order to establish and maintain a higher quality health service puts a major strain upon medical supply. As generalism atrophies away a larger number of sub-specialist medical teams are needed to provide the essential minimum number of doctors to be able to offer a 24 hour service, in acute hospitals.

Furthermore, as specialism replaces generalism in hospital medicine more medical trainees are required and more specialist trained consultant time is needed to support those trainees, which in turn puts pressure on the amount of time available for clinical service in the hospital and exacerbates the overall labour supply problem. The increasing speed of this trend towards greater specialisation, justified by the need to practice modern first world medicine in the twenty first century, has been encouraged by the government in its anxiety to improve outcomes in priority services. But nowhere does there seem to be evidence that government has calculated the impact of this on the demand for medical staff. The result is that it again exacerbates the supply side deficit.

• The Gender Balance in Hospital Medicine

The rapid shift in the gender balance of those wishing to train in medicine has increased the medical supply shortfall. In the last decade we have seen a largely male profession turn into a largely female profession in the sense that when the present undergraduates and trainees are all in career posts we can already look forward to two thirds of hospital doctors being women and an even higher proportion in general practice. Women undergraduates and trainees are likely to take longer to go through training because more of them will opt for part time training posts and when they finally take consultant or GP posts a higher proportion of them will wish to have part time employment. There is of course absolutely nothing wrong with this personal lifestyle choice, and current patterns may indeed change. But for those responsible for medical supply in the NHS it must be a major concern, for as training posts are gradually increased in order to increase the supply of consultants this *very rapid* change in the gender balance delays and sometimes negates the careful planning for growth.

To make a more controversial point, if the gender balance continues to change at its current rate the government may be forced to use positive discrimination to ring-fence a proportion of posts for males to avoid medical supply going into reverse. Few people are interested in studying the effect of this change apart from those whose motives appear to be feminist, but there is a real need for its true effects to be built into current manpower calculations; both at undergraduate medical schools and at the Department of Health.

• Government's Response to the Crisis in Medical Supply

The government is now aware of the true extent of the medical supply crisis as witnessed by the increasing number of fairly desperate initiatives discussed below. But just how bad is the shortfall? Not surprisingly national labour statistics throw no light on the question. Government is happy to show that overall WTE medical numbers are still growing but this is nowhere balanced with figures for increasing demand and falling clinical productivity.

At one time published consultant and other medical vacancies were helpful except that trusts did not advertise for posts they could not fill. After 1997 Health Authority control of consultant appointments meant that these figures became even less reliable. Only unmet demand in the form of waiting lists gives some indication, but there are so many caveats with current figures that their use is strictly limited. In the end an interpretation of how the government reacts to the medical crisis is the best way of measuring its own view of seriousness. A series of reactions are listed below.

i A new Consultant Contract
A new consultant contract was needed even in 1997 and it gave the government a glorious opportunity to reach an accord with the medical profession that would find a way to incentivise the profession to meet the short and medium term supply side deficit. Instead Labour chose to focus upon its political targets of anti-elitism, control of hours and private practice. It finally produced proposals (in the guise of an NHS management initiative) that split the profession but were clearly rejected, leading to the resignation of the leader of the BMA negotiating team. At the 2002 BMA Annual Conference the junior doctors begged their consultants not to vote for it. In proposing an 8am – 10pm, 40-hour working week the government allied together the private practice interest with the growing number of women doctors opposed to the ending of the 9am – 5pm day. Cynically the contract included a clause to let existing consultants keep the old contract. Offering the option of selling out the next generation to save ones own lifestyle. This cynicism

69

rebounded. The older consultants ignored the bribes and voted for the future of the profession and their younger colleagues. It was a truly heroic and memorable outcome and demonstrated the total inadequacy of government labour supply policy.

Milburn's replacement by Reid has allowed the government an opportunity to climb down. By the end of July 2003 negotiations with the BMA gave the consultants virtually all of their requirements for the new contract. Even so, such was rank and file hostility to the government, that there was press speculation that the offer might still be rejected. Acceptance this autumn will give the government a breathing space in the short term. But if consultants interpret a new contract strictly there will be serious productivity concerns in the longer term. And there is hearsay evidence that many will retire once the salary and pension arrangements are in force. If this happens the supply side effect will be serious and it is clear that, despite a new contract, the government has not won hearts and minds. Dr Reid's concessions do not equate to a change of heart; but merely a tactical withdrawal.

ii Importing non-EU Doctors to Live and Work in the UK

Even before 1997 individual hospital trusts, specialist firms of head-hunters and opportunists had been trying to raid world medical supply to plug serious gaps in the UK. Some were able to come in at consultant level (e.g., many South Africans); more came to work as non-consultant career grades. (When Mandela met Major during the 1996 State Visit it is believed that he made a strong plea to stop this traffic.) Thus it was a surprise when New Labour eagerly adopted and extended the practice. Now high profile UK teams are seeking to recruit high quality, senior doctors to leave their domestic practice to come to the UK. This may achieve a short term alleviation in some high profile sub-specialties, but its effects will be limited and its costs high.

iii Using the Private Sector for NHS Work

2002 saw permission for trusts to contract with private hospitals to treat NHS patients in order to achieve waiting list targets. Launched as an important initiative it started to be downplayed in mid 2002 as the cost implications become more apparent. The option still exists but is not the current frontrunner.

iv Sending NHS Patients to Hospitals Abroad

2002 also saw permission to contract with EU hospitals for treatment abroad to achieve waiting list targets. Announced with a fanfare of publicity this initiative is also now being downplayed. Newer NHS guidance has limited its use as have the on-costs incurred in flights, hotel accommodation, family support etc., etc. As with option (iii) above the *real* costs of this option soon began to make it less attractive as a high volume solution.

v Bringing Surgical Teams to the UK on Short-Term Contracts

This was a third 2002 initiative that is still centre stage. At a particular level in the medical career structure there are doctors willing to travel and work for short holiday periods abroad for money at rates below average EU medical earnings; usually because these doctors cannot access this type of work in their own country. The final costs will be higher than currently calculated due to travel, accommodation and other social costs. St. Mary's Hospital in London has piloted this option for limited day case and overnight stay patients only, using doctors from medical schools with which they have long established contacts. This has potential viability where quality can be assured in advance and the motivations are more clinical than financial. This St. Mary's practice will not be transferable to a 'bog standard' DGH and the Royal College of Surgeons is right to be alarmed at the quality implications of this particular move.

71

2002 has seen a succession of initiatives, one after the other, in a shorter and shorter timescale. This is the best evidence yet that Milburn was aware of the sheer scale of the medical supply deficit. The very speed of new initiatives is suggestive of some degree of panic. Proposals to pay doctors not to retire early are also a sign that New Labour has not reinforced the commitment of medical staff to NHS working. (The Audit Commission Report on GPs in Wales in 2002 thought this initiative essential if numbers were not to stall and go into reverse due to the rise and rise in GPs opting for part time work.) There is finally, the strange case of the Spring 2002 Royal College of Radiologists' Report into the severe and immediate staffing crisis in radiology that somehow never got to the public's attention.

The 2001 Audit Commission Report, 'Review of National Findings for Medical Staffing', published in 2002 reinforces the evidence of supply crisis. It concluded that many doctors were being forced to act as specialist registrars without appropriate qualifications; that many trusts were not New Deal compliant; and that medical employment per 1000 attendances varied widely, particularly between similar smaller acute trusts.

Labour Substitution

It is difficult to treat this subject properly in a chronological approach. Labour substitution to relieve the pressure of medical work has been underway for well over a decade and is one of the options supported by all governments to help overcome medical supply problems. Much of the success in the period is due to co-operation between the professions rather than to political initiatives. There are now many examples and all appear to be benefiting health care provision and patient services. They key to success has been the provision of post basic and specialist training to other professional staff to allow role expansion both to work alongside doctors and to take independent responsibility for a segment of work previously done by doctors.

The enhanced working partnership occurs more frequently between doctors and nurses; in the sharing of clinic workload; in more recent teamworking in A&E; in relieving junior doctors of some theatre and other tasks etc. The aim is to select patients to make best use of consultant time while managing the continuing care of patients across a range of medical specialties. Perhaps the most controversial development has been in general practice with NHS Direct, and one suspects it is here to stay because GP supply is already so inadequate in many parts of the UK.

But labour substitution is much wider than nursing. In radiology radiographers are now clinically training to undertake a range of work including plain film reporting, barium examinations and now mammography reporting. In histopathology biomedical scientists are taking over many responsibilities in the preparation of slides for consultant reporting. Therapeutic radiographers, physiotherapists and others are all involved in initiatives to a greater or lesser extent. Labour substitution is one important contribution to the struggle to meet workload demands but it is limited in its overall potential. Almost all of these professions face their own labour supply difficulties and several localities are already facing such crises. Substitution can only achieve so much and these issues are addressed further in later sections of this chapter.

Conclusion

All the evidence suggests that the government has remained committed to its determination *not* to seek an accord with the medical profession about how best to expand and improve medical services in the UK. There is a very real feel that the Prime Minister imposed this upon a (probably willing) Milburn as a sine qua non of policy. In the last five years the CMO has been stripped of medical manpower responsibility; College advisors to CMOs in the old style have gone; Postgraduate Deans no longer manage and direct senior training; the Medical Royal Colleges are no longer alone responsible for medical quality and competence through the removal of the STA (Special Training Authority); the originally rejected contract would have controlled hospital consultants, fixed their working hours and effectively barred new consultants access to private practice. Additionally the approach to the staffing crisis has been to try to by-pass UK doctors, UK training and UK standards with a greater and greater proportion of non-UK doctors who are expected to be more amenable to firm management control and supervision. Finally, if in August 2004 the government really tries to implement the Working Time Directive, full shift working will force a change in our renowned and high quality approach to medical training and transform it into the mainstream EU model. But without the rest of the European health superstructure it is not workable in the UK, not to mention the quality losses.

The prospect is disturbing. Alternative medical supply from *any* source is too fragile for the government to be able to achieve a supply solution without the active support of the UK medical profession. But the price of that support would eliminate most of its long term (and unquestionably anti-doctor) agenda. To the government doctors are 'good guys' only if they do medicine 'our way'. A few are already willing and co-operative but the mainstream of the profession is not on board as the original contract rejection showed. Dr Reid's appointment as successor to Milburn created an opportunity for the government to back down. But his tactical withdrawal on the contract will still not be the partnership on medical terms necessary to help alleviate the immediate crisis and could instead lead to many older consultants taking their pension and going.

To prove success with their labour supply strategy the government have to show that the workload backlog in the NHS is coming down. This makes waiting list figures crucial. But 'genuine' waiting list numbers are hidden (e.g. to access radiology modalities); the rules of the current system understate the numbers waiting (difficulties in getting onto a waiting list, ease of reasons for being taken off etc); and

clinical priorities are suppressed (to make *length* of wait the only priority). But the current waiting list system is the only universally recognised public record of NHS success or failure, despite the growing plethora of standards and targets. The government cannot succeed
, if waiting list numbers go into reverse, but rapidly rising clinical demand; the greater public expectation of treatment, and the many legitimate reasons why consultant productivity will stall, mean that the waiting list targets will fail because medical supply cannot at present keep pace without genuine trust between the government and the doctors. If desperate chief executives pressure the doctors too much it will lead to revolt or desertion. The government appears to have trapped itself into an unwinnable conflict because despite the contract it has not changed its long term desire to bring the doctors to heel.

There are also parallels here with the management of GPs. After an even longer negotiation than the consultants a new draft contract, amongst other things, switches the payment incentives from work volumes to work quality with some subjective measures of quality such as patient approval. Only half the GPs voted for the original draft principles and the BMA suspended the vote to clarify 'adverse' clauses in the proposed contract. The government was forced to give more money guarantees before the contract was accepted. It had no option. Many GPs were threatening to leave general practice because the workload and the current GP shortages have already placed services in many areas on a knife edge. (Lists of 3,800 in the north east are not tenable.) The government got its vote but will it retain the older GPs? If in the next two to three years they opt to go it will represent the end of universal medical cover in general practice. So much for choice!

3 The Shortage of Nurses
Background
As with doctors there is a historical background some of which is essential to understanding the current dilemmas and limited options. The issues relevant to this analysis are listed as a series of bullet

points below, but they do not constitute a comprehensive historical analysis.

- **Nurse Training**

  The most important and the longest of these background factors concerns the way nurses used to be trained and the way they are trained now. Nurses used to train in Schools of Nursing based at all the principal hospitals across the country. More recently, under this system, they entered at 16 as pupil nurses (not many) or at 18 as student nurses. Immediately their time was divided between work on the wards alongside trained nurses and more formal teaching in the local schools of nursing. As a consequence of this contract they received a modest salary right from the start. They lived at home or in student nurse accommodation on the hospital site. Entry at 18 required two 'A' levels or equivalent and in the latter days of this system local colleges were allowed to prepare applicants, without the 'A' levels, for an equivalent entry examination. Once qualified, nurses could undertake many training programmes to qualify them to undertake advanced nursing commitments e.g. in ITU nursing. These courses were nationally sanctioned and supervised by the Nurses' National Training Boards. **One of the great assets of this system was that it allowed 18 year old, (mainly), girls with a strong sense of commitment to 'caring' to become immediately involved in the caring process with patients at the bedside.**

The Royal College of Nursing (RCN), which like the BMA is a trade union as well as a professional body, had been campaigning for a radical change in the training system for some years and achieved a political commitment from the Conservatives two decades ago to introduce reforms known as 'Project 2000'. The RCN's motivation for the Project 2000 campaign was multifactorial. There was a desire to strengthen the academic base in nursing from the limited number of existing University post-graduate nursing departments. There was a need to extend post-

76

qualifying education to introduce greater specialisation into nursing and an extended nursing career structure. In addition Project 2000 was part of a campaign to raise the status and income of nurses. Enhancing the academic requirement of nursing qualifications and extending the career structure was very much part of a campaign to re-position nurses relative to doctors, in order to change the pay relationship.

When introduced Project 2000 faced many problems which had a significant negative impact upon nursing supply.

i The three year academic programme was university or college based leading to a qualifying degree or equivalent. The programmes were based away from hospitals; Schools of Nursing closed; students were no longer paid but, initially got a small 'grant', and the first 18 months were in full time lecture room tuition before nursing students started to spend part of their second 18 months as supernumeries on hospital attachments. This quite dramatic and sudden change in nurse training had some immediate negative effects on supply. It cut the flow of applicants with a strong motivation to care for patients. The 18 months academic work led to a major fallout from training in the early years. Those that stayed the course were the ones motivated to achieve academic success and who felt comfortable in the full time classroom environment.

If we take more recent statistics of this effect from the United Kingdom Central Council for nurse etc training (UKCC) Statistical Register, initial entries to the nursing register (allowing UK practice) from UK training fell by 36% from 18,980 to 12,082 between 1990/91 and 1997/98. (Of the 36%, 26% represented the numbers dropping out during training or failing to register as a nurse after training and 10% represented a fall in nurse training places over the period.) Between 1997 and 2000 Labour has increased training places, but the maximum final year student numbers have only risen from 11,566 to 15,478 between 1997 and 2000 and those who actually registered will be somewhat less than the 15,478 which compares unfavourably with the 18,980 that registered in 1990/91. Labour have improved the numbers in the system; and have cut the very high fall out rate, but the net numbers registering as nurses is still way below 1990/91. Of those that register some will not practice in the UK and a small but increasing number will go straight to private nursing.

In summary, Project 2000 failed to introduce changes to nurse training in a sensitive way; and failed to give priority to the maintenance of nursing supply to the NHS. Project 2000 was an 'own goal' which is threatening labour supply by its immediate impact upon numbers and by its longer term impact upon the age balance within the working profession.

ii Recent reforms of the training structure have meant introducing the students to the work on the ward more quickly and breaking up the programme blocks between classroom and hospital. This may have helped the recent reduction in the high fallout rate, in which case it points clearly to the errors in the initial Project 2000 scheme.

iii A more worrying criticism of Project 2000 is that is has trained chiefs, who, on qualification, find themselves to be indians and that this has led to early, disillusionment and withdrawal from nursing. Anecdotal evidence supports this but there is no published data to back it.

● **Nursing Management**
The last twenty years have seen a substantial change in the ward nursing hierarchy. The ward sister used to manage the ward *and* all

the nurses who worked on it who were thus part of a single, managed, ward based team. (The same applied to clinic teams.) Since then ward nurses have metamorphosed several times to become increasingly independent in the management of their own group of patients with less flexibility to work as one ward team. This has also made junior doctor/nurse working less productive. In fairness to the nursing profession the wider mix of patients on each ward contributes to this and without making value judgements either way it is enough to say that this system is more doctor and nurse intensive at a time of poor supply, even if the claims for quality improvement are correct.

The Demographic Time Bomb

- Nursing supply in the UK faces a demographic catastrophe due to the failure to take emergency action to redress the effect of Project 2000 on the number of nurses qualifying:

	Age Band	NHS Nurses by Headcount
1	< 29	48,313
2	30 – 39	92,660
3	40 – 49	81,145
4	50 – 59	43,224
5	60+	4,236

Source : D of H 2001 non-medical workforce census.

Most newly trained school leaver nurses enter NHS employment in their 21st year and the first age band is therefore seven and a half years rather than ten. Even so the scale of the gap between Project 2000 volumes and previous volumes is clear. To maintain nursing numbers, not to increase them, would have required age band one to have in the order of 70,000 nurses not 48,313; and this would make no allowance for the rising level of annual demand *plus* the effects of labour substitution by nurses, *and* dispersal into non-practice nursing jobs. The contribution of Project 2000 shows up more strongly if we split age band 2; age 30 – 34, 41,445, age band 35 – 39, 51,215. The over 35s were overwhelmingly trained prior to Project 2000. Even the 40 – 44 band is 46,116; well above the annual rate for age band 1. The nursing profession itself and the RCN in particular are responsible for the failure to act on Project 2000. What better than a labour supply crisis to push up nursing incomes? And it was the Prime Minister himself who dramatically intervened on television in January 2000 to offer the new grade of consultant nurse pay of up to £40,000 p.a. This was a clear indication of government anxiety at the state of nursing supply. Finally the reader should remember that these figures include foreign nurses coming to the UK, overwhelmingly below the age of 35, and that if demographic data for foreign nurses was available it would sharpen the effect of the Project 2000 shortfall. The NHS needs 25,000 nurses a year coming out of UK domestic training and into the NHS if it is to fill the hole in the 21 – 35 age range and contribute to rising demand, or there will be meltdown at the end of the decade. Project 2000 as currently reformed cannot do that. The NHS is currently being kept going by nurses aged over 40 with traditional, pre-Project 2000 training; half the total labour force!

- **Alternative Sources of Nursing Supply**
  There are a number of other sources of trained nurses apart from the immediate employment of newly qualified UK nurses.

i The most traditional is that of bank nurses – qualified nurses not in regular employment but willing to be offered short attachments in a local staffing crisis. Between 1997 and 2000 the total national number of bank staff has remained constant at between 8,500 and 9,500 WTEs. (UKCC figures Sept. 2001). They form around 3% of total staffing but have not been capable of expansion in recent years.

ii Campaigns to get trained nurses in the UK to return to NHS employment – almost choosing their own hours – have had publicity and some early success, but anecdotal evidence is that many have left after limited periods. Frustratingly there is no nationally available data on those coming in and those leaving within, say, three years. The lack of published data suggests that this is not seen as a strategically successful contribution to closing the supply side deficit.

iii Agency nursing by contrast has been a lifesaver to many hospitals, particularly in the south east. Expenditure on agency nursing staff in England more than doubled between 1997 and 2000, from £154M to £334M. In very broad terms this constitutes 16,700 WTE nurses on average every day of the year, (based on a £20,000 gross cost), or 6.5% of total English supply. The concentration of these nurses in the south east (many are non-UK citizens) suggests very high agency dependency in that area and individual London hospitals are known to reach 30% dependency. Agency nurse spending as a proportion of total nurse spending in London Trusts has now reached 40%. In nine years it has risen from 30% to 40% (Deeming). Much agency work is also done by *UK* nurses seeking higher income.

iv The final additional source of nurses is by import. Foreign nurses coming into the UK rose to 14,035 by head count in 2001/02 (Nursing and Midwife Council), half from the Philippines. If this source of supply is sustained it could make a major contribution to avoiding any future demographic time bomb, but there are important caveats.

❖ We do not know how many are staying and how many are returning home within what periods of time.

❖ We do not know how sustainable is this volume year on year. Are the higher numbers of 2000 – 2002 an immediate mopping up of available supply (and therefore drying up), and will volumes fall to much lower sustainable levels?

❖ How long can we justify 40% of these numbers coming from genuinely third world countries?

❖ 5.7% of these 14,035 have been calculated as being HIV positive (UNAIDS July 2002). Access to the UK for treatment is therefore one motive for responding to UK adverts. How much will health status and language weaknesses undermine the more positive view of importation?

Despite all these caveats importation is currently staving off an immediate *unmanageable* supply deficit, but we lack published data on its sustainability, over what period. Reliance on this source on present data is at best brittle.

- **Factors Affecting the Solution to the Nursing Supply Deficit**
  The reader is asked to judge the seriousness of the situation from the above analysis and the following data.

  i From 1997 to 2001 qualified nursing employment by UK WTEs has risen from 217,940 to 237,410, or 8.9% averaging 2.2% p.a. (D of H Statistical Bulletin Feb 2002). Of these 1,150 WTEs went to work in NHS Direct reducing the traditional nursing supply increase to 8.5% or 2.1% p.a.

  ii During this period officially advertised nursing vacancies have risen to 3.75% of WTE posts, and in London the figure is 6.1% (D of H Health Vacancies Survey 2001).

- Agency nurse spending has risen year on year with a 117% rise over this four year period 1997-2001! 37% of agency spending is due to vacancies and 45% due to leave (28% sick leave). (Audit Commission 2001).

- In the UK the number of nurses per 1,000 population has fallen to 4.25 in 2000 compared with 5.25 in 1991. In 2000 France was above 6.0 and Germany was over 9.0. (OECD health data 2002).

- The D of H figures *include* all qualified nurses working at *any* job in the NHS including all managers who happen to be nurses. The Department does not break down these figures but anecdotal estimates suggest that the increase in qualified nurses working outside clinical practice could consume the whole of the actual nursing WTE growth between 1997 and 2001. This worsening of supply relative to demand has all happened despite the flow of imported nurses and therefore suggests that at current levels the imports are not stabilising the deficit, let alone filling it. Finally, there is all the subjective evidence published from newspapers and journals implying that stress, over-work, isolated responsibility and long hours are causing many nurses to re-think their commitment to the profession.

Conclusion

To know the exact state of the nursing supply deficit and its nearness to breakdown it is necessary to know:

- nursing WTEs less those no longer in direct clinical nursing posts;

- the demographic structure of the profession;

- the current pattern of age related withdrawal/retirement from the NHS;

- the current annual supply trends.

It is then necessary to factor in the annual growth in demand for clinical nursing provision and for nurses being drawn into posts that are not specifically nursing. Not all of this data is collected although it could be; but one thing is regrettably certain, this data will not all be put in the public domain unless it reads positively. Much of the 'negative' data quoted here comes from non-D of H sources. The current Annual Report of the D of H simply records a continuing growth in unspecified nursing posts.

But on *all* the current trends for which hard data has been used the immediate prospect is for a gradual widening of the supply deficit leading to an unavoidable breakdown when the worst of the 'demographic time bomb' starts to rapidly erode nursing numbers by the end of the decade. This breakdown will take the form of hospital by hospital crises forcing the transfer of core nursing duties to task trained, but professionally unqualified, staff. Some would argue that this is happening already; beyond the areas of agreed labour substitution on the wards. Only a substantial and sustained increase in UK training supply can stop this happening. Yet applications are currently just below one per vacancy and more radical training solutions would mean a major fight with the RCN. Unfortunately for the government it has chosen to play 'Mr Nice Guy' with the nursing profession in order to help it win its battle with the doctors. Which precludes the necessary reform of radically tackling Project 2000. Instead we have expensive media campaigns to recruit 8000 nursing and midwifery trainees per year - anything but the necessary reforms to the system!

4 Labour Supply Challenges in Other NHS Professions

Midwifery
Midwives used to have to train as nurses first before doing their midwifery qualification. This re-inforced their long held status as independent practitioners in their own right in the same way as

doctors and dentists. Anyone reading the 1946 Act, which set up the NHS, cannot fail to notice how much of it is given over to regulating the relationship between doctors and midwives in the exercise of their independent practitioner roles. With the advent of Project 2000 students were allowed direct entry to midwifery training without requiring a first qualification in nursing. At first this brought more people into midwifery training and as the new midwives could not 'transfer back' into nursing the signs were positive about sustaining midwifery supply.

The next strategically important step for midwifery was the Conservative government's introduction of 'Changing Childbirth' which, among other things, developed the role of the midwife relative to the GP and obstetrician in the guidance of pregnant women through pregnancy, childbirth and during the baby's first year. This required a greater commitment to community midwifery emphasising that childbirth was a natural phenomenon that should not automatically be handled in the 'illness model' of doctors. The ideal was that community midwives had their clients from pregnancy, went into the labour ward with them, and then remained as their post-natal contact for up to a year. This involved guidance about whether and when to contact 'the medical team'.

This development split the profession into two; the community midwives who did far less delivering of babies and the hospital based delivery suite midwives with the best developed practice of coping with difficult deliveries. It is also a labour structure that reduced the productivity of the WTE midwife from the mid-40s deliveries per WTE midwife p.a. to just below 30 deliveries and falling. Some trusts now average just less than 20 deliveries a year per WTE midwife. (In fairness to midwives, the community midwife has now taken on an important part of the work of health visitors during the first year after childbirth).

Subsequent to these changes labour supply in midwifery has fallen and the Royal College of Midwives (RCM) is now talking, justifiably, of a midwifery supply crisis.

- In the four years from 1998 – 2001 midwifery WTEs in NHS employment fell from 18,170 to18,050, a fall of 0.67%.

- The demographic structure of midwifery is only available when combined with health visitors (midwives being three-quarters of the total). The combined *headcount* figures are:

Age	Number
<29	2,321
30 – 39	10,809
40 – 49	12,621
Over 50	8,235

No fewer than 25% are already over 50 and 62% are over 40; only 6.8% are below 30! These are the classic ingredients of an imminent labour supply crisis; but childbirth volumes have been static, unlike the rising demand for nursing. Despite this the threat of 6,000 midwives being lost to the midwifery labour force in five to ten years would make the current role of midwives unsustainable.

- The RCM has recently been concerned that relatively newly employed community midwives have been leaving the profession and, amongst other things, complaining of bullying. They do not have the same level of clinical experience of delivery as their hospital based colleagues and their role in the delivery suite for 'their mothers' has sometimes been less clinically adept giving rise to 'us' and 'them' situations. The majority of community midwives are the younger post-Project 2000 staff. If they leave in any significant numbers the demographic staffing crisis would be unmanageable. If they are asked to increase their delivery room experience they may also leave, because a proportion of the new entrants to midwifery are focused on the care of the post-natal baby and see that as their principal job satisfaction.

From a purely labour supply perspective the position in midwifery is one of the most serious in the NHS and, if anything, they have a more serious agency dependency than in nursing. Even at present levels the issue makes a contribution to rates of timed caesarean operations and may force this rate to rise as the shortage gets worse. No-one has collected the *really* critical data; the age of the delivery suite midwives. With so much attention given to other NHS staffing crises, one gets the impression that in midwifery, the eye is off the ball!

Laboratory Scientists

Clinical and Biomedical Scientists work in each of the main sub-specialties in pathology. Most hospitals have four main sub-specialties but in specialist tertiary hospitals this can extend to five, six or even seven separate departments. Internationally this staffing is less fragmented and e.g., in the USA there is just one division in training between clinical and anatomical pathology.

The NHS laboratory service provides us with a textbook example of what happens to staffing when labour supply shortage hits meltdown. In 1988/89 at the height of the Lawson boom the private sector lured away large numbers of relatively poorly paid biomedical scientists and left gaping holes in the staffing of several laboratories, mainly across the south and east of England. An emergency national agreement carried through the introduction of an unskilled worker, the medical laboratory assistant, and MLAs, as they are universally known, were literally pulled off the streets in quite large numbers relative to the total staffing of laboratory departments. This happened to a greater extent in clinical than in anatomical pathology but the recruitment was significant and rapid. The focus was upon freeing up the time of the biomedical scientists to undertake the essential professional duties that could not be done without the right scientific skills. The NHS then rapidly invested in improved automation and MLAs became machine feeders and minders. The MLAs role has developed over the last decade with the introduction of a wider range of support functions, and even in microbiology departments, where tasks are the least automated within clinical pathology, they now number roughly half of the total staffing.

One of the lessons to be learned from this experience is that in the early response to the staffing crisis the ability to automate functions made an important contribution to the success of the new and much altered staffing structure. Without the ability to automate the transition would have been much more difficult to achieve and even today the histopathology (anatomical pathology) departments; that are not automated and rely on the combination of scientific skills and manual dexterity; have the smallest proportion of MLAs. For professions without the ability to automate part of their function such a rapid transition is much more difficult.

One would have expected that the change in the staffing structure in pathology in the early 1990s would have led to improved grading opportunities for biomedical scientists whose work became more scientifically focused and who acquired responsibility for the supervision of the MLA team. Unfortunately for the biomedical scientists and ultimately for the NHS this did not happen to any degree and the laboratory service ended the 1990s in a very unstable labour supply position. There are a number of factors that account for this.

- The requirement for a university scientific qualification means that laboratories are competing with the private sector to recruit suitably qualified staff. When starting salaries for scientists, even with higher degrees, can be as low as £12,000 p.a., and far below the supplements being offered to new school teachers in the sciences, it is easy to understand why recruitment is difficult. The number of trainee biomedical scientists is at present too low to sustain the existing labour force and the problem is not being seriously addressed.

- My own research in 1999 and 2000 shows that some pathology laboratory departments have an 8 to 9% turnover of biomedical scientists and that many of these people are leaving relatively early in their NHS career. Current training rates will not sustain this degree of labour turnover.

- Hospitals depend upon a 24 hour on-call service by clinical pathology services. These are not tasks that can be performed by MLAs because staff working alone have to be responsible for much more independent scientific judgement and many departments are already at the critical stage in terms of their ability to sustain the 24 hour service for seven days a week. Again, the Working Time Directive is totally unhelpful to the traditional pattern of emergency on-call working and the substitution of the traditional system with shift working will require many more staff than are currently available.

- The annual turnover position amongst MLAs in the NHS is horrendous and for once the evidence really does justify the adjective. Private research evidence in 1999 and 2000 showed that across a range of nearly one hundred NHS laboratories MLA turnover was averaging 18%. Even in 2002 their income remained firmly below £10,000 per year and it is clear that most people in MLA employment form part of a transitory population that can move easily between jobs. This gives biomedical scientists a major annual challenge in training and retraining MLAs for the task that they perform. A little progress is being made in training the better MLAs to stay longer with slightly enhanced remuneration but an annual turnover of a fifth of the team illustrates how modest that progress has been.

The evidence above shows that a labour supply crisis in pathology can begin very quickly and escalate to the point of a systems failure within twelve months. If competitive and private sector recruitment pulls away the MLAs there is no other line of defence. Further, the *present* turnover of biomedical scientists is greater than those entering training and they no longer have the capacity to sustain the service in the event of a major downturn in MLA employment.

Radiographers

At the beginning of the NHS radiographers did little more than work in X-Ray rooms. Today they provide specialist radiographic services across a wide and growing range of modalities. X-Ray, fluoroscopy and ultrasound now sit alongside nuclear medicine, CT scanning, MR scanning, and radiographers also support a wide range of interventional services that continue to grow in volume and complexity. On top of this radiographers are vital to the breast screening service which is another area of continuing substantial growth in workload.

Therapeutic radiographers have different training and work separately in an almost equivalent range of radiotherapy and allied services. The two types of radiographers, diagnostic and therapeutic, work separately in different departments and do not overlap.

The demand for radiographers has grown as has the skills required of them and it will not surprise readers to know that radiography like other NHS professions has a serious labour supply problem. As with the other professions this is variable across the country but serious primarily in the south and east of England. Radiography like biomedical science in pathology has at present a worsening supply position and has the capacity to worsen rapidly but not with the same degree of instability as pathology. The issues are summarised below.

• Like biomedical scientists radiographers have not benefited from higher pay and greater national pay publicity in the way that nurses have.

- An additional drain on traditional radiographer supply is role expansion due to labour substitution. The scarcity of consultant radiologists is without doubt the highest proportionate scarcity of any main medical specialty. Sensibly, the response of the government and the professions has been to establish a national agreement ('The Red Book Agreement'), to provide for the additional clinical training of radiographers to undertake a range of traditional medical reporting tasks. This use of skills mix is essential if we are to avoid the collapse of the radiology service in the medium term. Gradually radiographers are being trained to undertake plain film reporting, barium studies and non-obstetric ultrasound services to release radiologists to focus on the rapidly growing volume of work in other modalities, such as MRI and upon the rapidly growing demand for interventional work. Unfortunately there is not a sufficient supply of radiographers to maintain radiographer workload and any significant shift towards 'clinical' radiography (replacing doctors) will cause significant gaps in supply at local level.

- The shortage of ultrasonographers is again more evident in the south and east of England but there are hospitals, including teaching hospitals, that have reduced the obstetric scanning of normal pregnancies to just a single scan because of the lack of staff to provide the traditional service. In other parts of the country normal pregnancies could expect two or three scans over the period of gestation. Between 1998 and 2000 the author has undertaken research in radiology departments where even *inpatients* have waited two weeks for a CT scan caused by a lack of staff not a lack of equipment. One harrowing meeting with young SHOs ended with one young woman doctor in tears about the death of elderly patients whose admission had merely been to

91

try to speed up the CT scan. Behind this are the endless and rising delays for outpatient access to a range of modalities. Only by failing to collect waiting list data for diagnostic procedures (including endoscopies in other clinical services) can the government hide its most intractable waiting list problems.

- Radiography has not admitted the support worker role in the way the role of the MLA has developed within the laboratory. There are support workers in radiography under a variety of different names, such as "helpers" or "aides", but their volume is certainly less than 10% of the qualified radiographer labour force. There is much debate in the profession about the potential role of 'imaging technicians' whose major contribution would be that they would be allowed to give ionising radiation to patients for simple x-rays but under supervision. The issue of, "..whose hand is on the button..", has become an emotive one and the Society of Radiographers (both the professional body and the trade union for radiographers) has so far stalled on the development of this role ; which would have the benefit of freeing up radiographers to develop their clinical radiography role if the NHS is capable of finding another source of rapid labour supply as in the case of MLAs. The Society has agreed, experimentally for a support worker role in breast screening because this is a particular area of labour shortage.

- For the five years between 1995 and 2000 the author has studied detailed research returns from roughly one hundred hospital trust radiology departments across the country. The lack of radiographers/ultrasonographers is not uniform between hospitals as there is a multiplicity of factors affecting the choice of radiographers about where they wish to work, but over the five year period the position of the bottom quartile of departments with the greatest labour problems has got worse almost year on year to the point where they are severely hampered in delivering a clinically acceptable service; and this quartile includes teaching hospitals and not just small acute hospitals with an uncertain future. Ultrasonography is a particular concern.

5 Conclusion

The objective of this chapter has been to try to identify the extent of the labour supply deficit, choosing medicine, nursing, midwifery, laboratory science and radiography where the most serious deficits exist. Serious in the sense that each professional service could cause a total breakdown in NHS provision if the supply deficit rises above a critical level. This is not to imply that other specialist services do not have their own supply problems, e.g., in mental health nursing or other professionals allied to medicine.

Frustratingly there are gaps in the data which make the size of the deficit virtually impossible to measure accurately. The most important and confusing gap is the measurement of staffing alongside rising demand because there is *no* measure, and no government desire to measure publicly the extra requirements of rising demand. Only the professions and the trades unions are motivated to make this analysis . To take the example of nursing we know from published data that in the four years to 2001 WTE nursing supply rose by 2.2% p.a. including the big rise in imports. On the demand side we know that NHS Direct took 0.1% of this rise. Over the four years many nurses moved to managerial posts outside nursing, and there is no national data on this. Nor is there any on the effect on labour supply of broader labour substitution into other clinical work. The true extent of labour scarcity depends on knowing both sides of the supply/demand equation, but the government is happier to focus solely upon rising staffing totals in its public presentation.

In private, government must be testing the demand side implications and in nursing it has panicked twice over nursing supply.; first in January 2000 over the dramatic £40,000 consultant nurse broadcast; and in the summer of 2002 over the publicity for its new drive for high levels of nursing imports. In the spring and summer of 2002 the same panic was evident over medical supply and the waiting lists; with three initiatives in quick succession; using capacity in the private sector; sending patients abroad, and then the importation option used in nursing. As the private measurement of the consequences of rising demand look dire, so the rate of public initiatives and their publicity grows. Clearly the news was bad in 2002/03.

Across the professions it is possible to extract a number of events which contribute to the poor prognosis in the short and medium term.

- The demographic trends do not help the government. In nursing and midwifery it shows rising dependence upon the over 40s and over 50s and in midwifery the demographic data is truly horrendous. In medicine it shows a retiring generation dominated by full time males and a new generation in which women predominate and with a rising proportion opting for part-time. The position is most critical in general practice where the clinical and linguistic demands of the post make importation a less viable option.

- There are sectors of high volatility to labour turnover; professional staff go into the private sector; they enter community practice in the local government sector; take early retirement or leave due to disillusionment, or over-work etc. Laboratory MLAs, for whom data is available, show the highest volatility amongst support workers. Reliance upon importing professional staff increases volatility, and finally the growing day by day dependence upon agency staff creates high volatility because it includes a significant proportion of younger people from abroad who are known to be transient, and where longer term supply cannot be guaranteed. Finally, in early 2003 the BMA indicated the high volatility of consultant employment when a national poll showed 25% of consultants considering leaving the NHS if a proper contract was not offered.

- The EU Working Time Directive is uniquely disadvantageous to the UK. With almost the smallest professional staffing relative to population the UK dependence upon 'overtime ' in all its guises is greater than in the rest of the EU. In addition the UK NHS and its professions are *structured* around a pattern of longer hours and for diagnostic departments they are essential. The government saw the chance of the Working Directive to 'break the mould' in medicine and went for it. This is probably the greatest single error of judgement in health policy by the post 1997 Labour government. August 2004 now gives us a breakdown of service date. A growing number of senior medical retirements will be fixed for July 31 2004. The Directive victimises the UK because our unique staffing structure cannot sustain the continental philosophy of low working hours policed by statute.

- The labour substitution initiative, vital for the longer term, is stalling due firstly to the lack of supply in the professions which are meant to develop their 'clinical' roles from medicine. Secondly, and more controversially, it lacks labour substitution *below*. In other words success requires the nursing, midwifery and radiographic professions to relinquish territory to support workers on the scale necessary to release professional staff to provide substitution for doctors. It is a moot point why the government has not pressed these professions as strongly as it has pressed doctors. One explanation, developed earlier in the chapter, is that for political reasons the government has first wanted to sort out and strengthen its control of doctors before showing its hand with the other professions.

- There is evidence above that the government has identified medicine and nursing as the strategically important professions and has concentrated its attention and initiatives in this area. There is no question that medical and nursing initiatives are needed, but in NHS service provision the smaller professions are vital to the

95

delivery of medical and nursing services; no more so than in diagnostics. The failure to address labour supply challenges in laboratory science and radiography has been a major mistake; (even the laboratory modernisation initiative has been a cost reduction exercise rather than a focus on labour supply). In therapeutic radiography this has been an even greater mistake because of the profession's role in the cancer initiative. And in midwifery no-one seems to have thought through the sheer scale of the political damage when the service starts to buckle.

What surprised me most when Labour came to power in 1997 was their complete lack of understanding of the nature and complexity of labour supply in the clinical professions. Dobson acted more like a political old pro', kept Calman and did not try to smash up a labour supply system he did not understand. With Milburn all such restraint was abandoned. Calman was removed, his successor was barred from the subject, and the whole structure was taken apart and re-modelled in a way that had more to do with sorting out the doctors than with labour supply. The government then failed to match new targets with the ability to deliver supply. Labour did not seem to grasp that substantially improved clinical outcomes meant greater clinical specialisation which pushes medical consultant generalists faster towards extinction. It certainly did not understand the clinical training and supply implications of a *series* of promised improvements in clinical services. As a consequence it speeded up the eventual longer term supply failure. Another major error of understanding/judgement was its lack of appreciation of the clinical position of diagnostic services in delivering three of its four main clinical priorities.

There is still not a vision of the medical and wider clinical structure that the government wants to see in the next five to ten years; no comprehensive model to which they are aspiring; only the promise of big numbers that are not deliverable and which do not seem to fit together into a viable staffing structure for the future. Perhaps to

96

publish its vision would mean having to tackle all the professions simultaneously! Just to take medicine; a falling proportion of UK trained doctors; far more reliance upon temporary and permanent labour importation; more of the less adequately trained imports doing task orientated work in diagnostic and treatment centres; temporary purchases of EU doctors for one off contracts; and using European centres to export patients; does not all sit positively together as a future structure for UK medical care. Instead it is what it looks like; a temporary and botched together series of panic measures to try to bring the UK medical consultants to heel before the balloon goes up in August 2004. Is anyone placing bets?

CHAPTER 4
THE HEALTH AND SOCIAL SERVICES CONTINUUM

1 Introduction

This chapter deals with the contentious issue of social care and its interface with health care. Health is the responsibility of a Department of State and social care is the separate responsibility of local Social Services Authorities. (Housing and some other service funding belong to borough and district authorities where local government is two tier.) The current view of government and the Department of Health is that the health and social services continuum should indeed be a seamless service with local authorities ensuring that social services are pro-active in seeking to minimise hospital admissions and having systems to move acute hospital patients into appropriate social care settings without delay in discharge whenever such support is required.

The fact that health care is free and social care is means tested in a locally provided service means that the volume and quality of public services varies around the country. Social Services Authorities receive a grant from government to provide a range of primarily statutory social services. In recent years that grant has not kept pace with rising demand in most or all authorities. Local authorities then have to decide whether to limit services (perhaps simply by delaying client processing) or take from other local budgets; education, highways, libraries etc., or raise more Council Tax. The arcane funding system for local government complicates this issue of choice.

The Chancellor of the Exchequer's commitment to a 6% growth rate in this funding does not match the current annual rise in demand and does nothing to address the average level of overspending on these budgets, and this overspending cannot be sustained in the longer term. The unequal distribution of funding caused by the new 2003/04 local authority resourcing formula adds to this pressure because south-eastern authorities cannot now sustain both rising demand and regional rises in private sector service costs at only inflation level increases in funding. The Chancellor's response to this has been to proclaim a financial penalty on local authorities of £100 per night, (£120 in south east England), for every patient whose hospital discharge into the care of social services is delayed by more than three days, quaintly named 'a system of re-imbursement around discharge from hospital'. Despite some Department of Health pump priming money the Chancellor's objective is to bludgeon local authorities into using more of their own resources into guaranteeing an uninterrupted health and social services continuum. If Conservative County Councils have to raise more taxes the Chancellor would have no objection.

Unnecessary admission and delayed discharge affect both the efficiency and the cost of the NHS and this is why the Department of Health want local authorities to do more. In particular delayed discharge is seen as wasting acute bed resources and putting extra pressure upon existing acute hospitals. The seriousness of the issue of delayed discharge was the subject of a House of Commons Select Committee Report in 2002 and its recommendations will be considered later in the chapter. But there are broader policy issues and constraints that first need to be considered.

2 The Current Range of Social Care Provision

Patients discharged from hospital can be divided into three categories:

- Those that return to their home/family, voluntary carers without additional hospital or social services intervention; the majority of all discharges.

100

- Those transferred to a less acute NHS facility or service where any delay is handled within the NHS.

- Those requiring social services assessment and support to assist discharge.

'Patients' requiring assisted discharge become social services 'clients' on assessment and need assistance because of physical or mental disability/illness. The vast majority of these clients are over 75 and suffer chronic conditions either due to the ageing process or some specific clinical event such as a stroke.

These clients require support at one of a series of levels.

- The first is where the client's condition and lack of mobility requires the support of one or more of a mixed team of workers. This may be for the client's shopping, washing etc., meals on wheels or the attendance of staff to assist rising and dressing in the morning and again at night; or support if the client is singly or doubly incontinent or is unable to manage personal hygiene.

- The second is where the client requires direct commodities. These can be equipment; walking sticks, frames, wheelchairs etc.; and/or adaptations to the place of residence, e.g., ramps, stair rails, vertical lifts, adapted bathrooms; sometimes even the building of new ground floor rooms as a house extension.

- The third is where, over and above the first two categories, the client needs the environment of a sheltered housing community; a residential home; or a nursing home where regular nursing care is available rather than just social care.

The first category of support can be arranged as soon as a staff team can be put together. The second category takes longer; equipment can take weeks and the time for building adaptations can range from a month to eighteen months depending upon the extent of the changes required. The Disabled Facilities Grant is available up to £20,000 but the rules allow six months delay even for determination of the application. The third category can wait indefinitely, e.g., if there is no nursing home, or only one with no likelihood of vacancies due to waiting lists. Also, at present, a client can nominate a particular residential home and wait until space is available, knowing there is little immediate likelihood of a space. All these realities of provision sit uncomfortably alongside the Chancellor's decision to start fining local authorities on a daily basis if discharge delay exceeds three days.

One major reason why the system works at all is that the client can be in receipt of a poorer level of service than the one identified at assessment whilst waiting for the full social service package to be delivered. Being at home without a ramp, a lift, or bathroom adaptation and dependent upon greater voluntary carer support is a typical situation. But it may be that the home support from a work team is below assessment whilst waiting for new staff to be employed. Another reason is that hospitals can be more or less ruthless in their approach to discharge, sending clients home prior to assessment by social services, sometimes without even home support by the hospital.

A more positive picture, since the 1990s, is provided by the development of 'intermediate care' for which this government has made some specific provision in the form of extra grants into the system. 'Intermediate care' is harder to define in concrete terms because it covers a wide range of services. The unifying theme is that these services should either assist in avoiding hospital admissions or should avoid delayed discharge by providing some limited form of 'step down' from the acute hospital with rehabilitation support aimed at minimising the longer term support required. Several of these services are seen as providing support for up to six weeks whilst social services organise an appropriate longer term provision. Intermediate care can include beds, but is now focusing more upon support teams in the home. The continuing development of intermediate care will undoubtedly assist in the initial avoidance of delayed discharge, but if the resources are not to be tied down beyond six weeks social services still have to find and provide the care service requirement beyond that date. The PCTs clearly favour 'step-up' investment in a wide range of initiatives to prevent hospital admission, but the reality of limited resources and Labour's reimbursement charges will inevitably focus attention on step-down. The prognosis is not good because, as with the NHS, there exists a supply side deficit.

3 The Supply Side Deficit in the Provision of Social Care

Labour Supply

Labour supply problems beset the whole health and social services continuum and this is not helped by the fact that the NHS and local authorities, as two different employers, attempt to recruit competitively in a scarce labour market. Intermediate care health teams working in the community are trying to recruit social work support and there is always a need for local authorities to recruit nurses. Both employers have different terms and conditions of employment which adds to the tension at this competitive recruitment boundary. Beyond this there are specific shortages across the whole range of employee skills.

- Social workers
  Social workers and particularly social workers trained and experienced in elderly care hospital discharge cases are in short supply and in part this must be blamed upon a somewhat negative approach to social work by the previous government. As with nursing and related health professions the labour market is

experiencing acute under-supply. Posts cannot be filled, a large proportion of temporary staff from older commonwealth countries are employed (at least in the south east) and different local authority employers compete in different ways with packages to encourage recruitment. For example Essex County Council pays a £1,000 bonus and gives an extra day of annual leave on the completion of one year's employment and this is now rising to £2,000 and two days additional leave.

The other indications of labour scarcity and competition are that employers vary in their attitude to the size of the caseload held by social workers at any one time and some at least have traded down caseload size to encourage employment with the argument that this improves the quality of assessment. I have found active caseloads across the UK varying from 20 to 60 within a relatively small sample.

- Care Workers.
  Care workers are employed in support of the home care packages for discharged clients and in support of those clients who go to residential homes and nursing homes. Pay for care workers is variable and relatively low and their travel to work area is very limited, creating thousands of locally based labour markets with very different conditions. I have been given evidence from the north east and north west of the UK showing some difficulties but not serious ones in recruiting care workers. By contrast across the south and south east of the UK the local labour markets experience *extreme* labour supply shortage. It would not be an exaggeration to say that in the areas of most severe shortage, more than half of the patients requiring a care package to leave hospital experience some delay because of the lack of care workers. Tracing individual cases in one particular local authority suggests that a few patients never get discharged from hospital prior to death because of this difficulty. There are different reasons for this state of affairs and as always the reality is somewhat more complex than is at first apparent.

104

Care workers undertake two forms of support to a patient at home. They may do the shopping, collect the pension, do a very limited amount of basic housework, e.g. one hour a week (but this varies between local authorities) and they may undertake laundry depending upon the client's laundry arrangements. The second part of a care worker's role is to undertake personal care. They arrive to put the patient to bed at night and they arrive again in the morning to get the patient up and dressed. Many of these elderly patients are singly or doubly incontinent. It is easier to recruit people to do the former part of the task than to recruit people willing to undertake personal care. Few local authorities divide this work between different teams because of professional social work concerns about too many different people going into the house of an elderly and possibly confused person. Thus, when the advertised jobs encompass both roles it is harder and sometimes impossible to get recruits.

Care workers are available from two main sources:
- either as directly employed care workers on the local authority payroll or;
- from private agencies.

Those social workers concerned with the discharge of the elderly from the hospital in the south and south east of the country have had to rely more and more upon the ability of agencies to recruit staff and to take on a contract to provide a particular care package.

Some social workers specialising in the discharge of elderly patients from hospital are unable to use any other source of supply. The assessed client will not be discharged until a package can be staffed and with any more than a temporary delay the patient's condition in hospital can worsen to the point where they are withdrawn from discharge.

The existence of many thousands of local labour markets can create pockets of extreme shortage of supply even to the point of there being no care workers to serve anyone in a particular community. The lack of socially mixed housing in these communities is a factor.

Earlier in the chapter reference was made to intermediate care schemes that can take a care team into a client's home either to avoid a hospital admission or to assist a hospital discharge. These teams are meant to work for up to six weeks to facilitate these objectives but if they are to be of value they need to be free to move on to other clients in order to continue to assist the overall avoidance of admission or of discharge objectives. If the local authority is unable to find care workers for a needs assessed care package at the end of the six weeks this care intervention team is unable to move on or a client is left without the assessed service. There are no valid statistics locally or nationally on the extent to which these newer intermediate care initiatives are being stalled for this reason.

- Occupational Therapists
  Occupational therapists (OTs) were not considered in detail in Chapter 3, but in social care their role can be central. OTs and their assistants (OTAs) work in teams to identify and specify the equipment, adaptations and building/engineering needs of their clients. As with social workers, OTs are scarce; OTA support workers are used extensively, and in the south east there is a large transient professional population. In addition to income many social services departments use caseload to attract and retain staff. In Essex an OT will have a maximum caseload of eight new clients a month and a senior OT dealing with more complex cases only four per month, raising the salary cost per completed client case to above £1,000.

- Nurses
  Nurses are required in nursing homes and community social care teams. Chapter 3 analysed the problem of nursing supply in the NHS and this analysis applies equally in the social care sector.

Again, different employers have different terms and conditions of employment and here social care loses out to the NHS. One of the reasons social service clients can get no nursing home care is that there is either no local supply or so little that placement is impossible. It was against this background that the government promised to give free nursing care at an upper or lower assessment level to everyone 'needing' it. Lack of supply has kept the cost low!

4 The Lack of Residential and Nursing Home Places

The majority of residential and nursing homes are in the private sector and government policy is to speed up the transfer into the private sector by means of Best Value and other Reviews. The clear current objective is to achieve private sector status for at least the homes catering for the elderly (the main discharge blockage) within the next ten years. But the current lack of sufficient residential and nursing home beds is a national problem affecting virtually all parts of the UK. There are a number of reasons for this shortage.

- Increasing capacity requires the building of new homes or the purchase and renovation of other property. For any private sector organisation there are significant step costs to incur in doing this prior to the receipt of income for occupation. There is a risk involved in undertaking these step costs and the first serious element of that risk is the likely difficulty in recruiting care workers and, where appropriate, nurses, to ensure that the beds provided can be staffed.

- The private sector often needs to pay 'the going rate' for the locality to recruit staff and needs also to obtain what it believes to be an appropriate profit margin. The result of this is a level of cost per occupant per week which in many parts of the country is running well above the official weekly rates payable by local authorities. It is necessary to understand this costing system.

❖ If an assessment concludes that a client needs a residential home placement that assessment will include how much of the local authority payment will be recharged to the client after assessing the client's income and capital.

❖ In addition to this assessment the client may only be dischargeable to the residential home if a payment is made by the client to 'top up' the local authority contribution to the actual weekly charge in the residential home. (Sorting out these arrangements is another cause of delay in achieving discharge.) Local authorities have the power in individual cases to make supplementary payments above their standard payment to achieve residential home entry for particular clients. I find the selection basis for this to be both murky and variable. A more open alternative access policy is for the local authority to block contract with particular residential homes which will keep beds available for local authority clients in exchange for a contract price higher than the going local authority rate. There must be several variations of this as most authorities are experiencing placement difficulties.

Despite all this most private sector provision is at prices lower than those that local authorities can operate, staff and maintain for themselves, but there is weakness in the private system that has to be addressed. The imbalance of supply and demand creates a greater likelihood of profitability for the private sector but the risks of expanding provision are such that they need a very strong certainty of success. Governments come and go and the harshness or otherwise of the funding regime for local authority supported clients is an issue of total uncertainty. This is not only a reference to national government but to local government as well. A swing to the left in a big Conservative county could immediately raise fears that provision would swing back to the public sector with the ensuing risk to private providers whose staff would be the first targets of public sector recruitment.

Finally, residential and nursing homes provide places privately to the wealthier members of society. Their demand for places is set to increase for demographic reasons and those families seeking security for their older members can always outbid local authorities. Because these homes are in the private sector they will always prefer the higher profitability of the private client. The exception relates to residential and nursing homes whose quality and amenities make them less attractive to the wealthy private client. This is why such new provision as there is appears to be focusing on the top end of the market in terms of amenity costs although there are no national data to indicate the extent to which this is happening.

The Report of the House of Commons Select Committee in 2002 concluded that the supply deficit of all NHS, private and voluntary beds had increased due to a fall of 34,200 places between 1997 and 2001, and rejected the government's estimate of a fall of 19,000. This represents a fall of 6% capacity in four years against an unmeasured rising demand. The private and voluntary sectors have step-costs; uncertain access to labour and more recently the cost of meeting the building and staffing requirements of the Social Care Act 2000, which "wish list of perfection" in care has now had many of its clauses withdrawn or suspended. The fact that the government has had to do this within two years of the legislation indicates how concerned they have become about the falling supply of care beds.

Taken together the labour supply difficulties and the falling supply of care beds pose a serious policy dilemma for government. If care beds are insufficient an alternative strategy would be to rely upon more home care at a resource level to manage even the least mobile and most incontinent clients. In 2002 the government gave a clear policy steer towards a higher proportion of domiciliary care; and even the Select Committee gestured in this direction. This policy change, away from residential homes to home care, is itself interesting. It shows that social work assessment on the *location* of service is a value judgement that can be flexible as between residential homes or home care. There is no question that public opinion favours an open-ended right to residential support as the Prime Minister found out on an earlier 2002 television programme in which he faced this demand coming top of a patient/client priority list. Despite this the emphasis is being placed on home care and the House of Commons Select Committee Report argued that , "..closure of care home places can act as a further spur to the development of care at home and other responses tailored to the assessment and preferred choices of individuals." Preferred choices – but excluding care homes! There is also another element that influences these choices.

5 Means Testing Social Care

Clients in receipt of social care may be required to make a means tested contribution that varies according to the cost of the service provided. This involves both income and capital and in the case of residential or nursing home accommodation can involve the sale of the family home if only the client resides there. In the case of capital the client is supported once capital is eroded to £19,000 and in the case of income the resident may retain £16.80 per week with the rest of income being surrendered, if necessary, to meet weekly charges. This simple statement is complicated by the fact that benefits may or may not be withheld depending upon the type of social care received.

It is always necessary for the social worker to introduce the client to these rules and complexities. On visits to clients with social care staff as a county councillor I can witness to the fact that elderly people

110

being assessed are largely unaware of the payment rules or of how substantial their own contribution will be. Finally, patients/clients and their families currently have a right to choose which residential or nursing home they nominate and to which they may have to make means tested payments up to the local authority rate, knowing that this rate is too low for the nominated home and knowing that they can refuse 'top up' payments. Such patients/clients can be tempted to make 'unreasonable' choices of homes with no foreseeable chance of placement in order to try to remain in a free hospital bed.

The Select Committee were very coy about means testing. They did not explain and comment upon the means testing rules and even in their analysis of reasons for delayed discharge they fudged the extent to which means testing was the cause. The report identified 8.1% of delays as relating to this exercise of the right to choose a residential or nursing home. But one category involving 20.4% of all delayed discharges is described as, "..awaiting care home placement," which unquestionably includes cases influenced by issues of means testing. Significantly the Select Committee warmed to the idea of integrating health and social care and called for pilot studies to test the best ways forward using a lead commissioner model, but did not specify the implications of this for means testing.

The reason such attention has been given to the Select Committee Report here is that it gives credence to the myth that the integration of health and social care would have many benefits. To strengthen this argument the Report has almost totally ignored the issue of means testing. It is a simple impossibility to combine a free at the point of delivery health service with a means tested social service to create the government's seamless service where patient/client flows are not impeded.

At the point at which means testing kicks in (under current rules) the flow may have to stop. Patients/clients, their families, even their

111

solicitors may become involved in debates about what is and is not appropriate, what homes are 'suitable', what constitutes an appropriate home care package etc. The Chancellor's decision to fine local authorities after a three day delay, in isolation, does not remove this problem, but it does give wealthier patients/clients families the opportunity to hold a gun to social services and to bargain for greater public funding, for example, if grandma agrees to go to home X rather than home Y. Only those below the means testing thresholds can aspire to the seamless service under current rules; i.e. where health and social care are both free services. But to make *the whole* of social care free is beyond the capacity of this or any other UK government. Given that means testing stays there will always be a need for two administrative systems and there will always be some friction at the boundary in individual cases not least because clever clients and families will always try to play the system to avoid payment.

The Select Committee proposed changing the current rules to allow hospitals and social services to forcibly transfer patients/clients who had selected unattainable homes, into suitable, alternative, next best facilities on a 'temporary' basis until the home of choice was available. If this involves compulsory means tested payments in a home the patient/client is refusing to go to, it has no chance. Are we going to force people to pay for services they don't want? Yet to pay with public money for this 'temporary' home undermines means testing controls on public expenditure.

Many home care packages end up being negotiable, if only at the margin; the definition of the correct social care package is not subject to the same absolutes as the practice of clinical science. Families may not often question a clinical decision in hospital, but when it comes to what services are in the home they have very clear opinions and can speak with far greater authority. Despite all these difficulties and challenges the reader should be in no doubt that a strong case can be made to support the present health and social care divide on the basis that there may not be a better solution however untidy the current one may seem. The Scots bravely abandoned social care means testing and in a single year the costs escalated significantly. Demographic change and greater public awareness of 'the opportunities' will make the scheme fail within, at most, three years. But at least the case study will prove the point.

6 A Policy Option: Labour uses the choice weapon again

The government is encouraging another policy development. Why not give patients/clients the cash so that they can tailor-make the services *they* want in buying their own package or by retaining cash to allow a family member to provide social care? This creates 'choice' and avoids the bargaining referred to above. Social services would still assess the care package required in order to determine the cash payment and would have to make periodic visits to ensure that a service was being provided. This appears superficially attractive. Weekly cash in hand will be quite tempting to some families. The wealthier can be sent home with a list of what they should buy out of their own resources. And at a stroke the government is freed from the labour supply deficit. The government has given you the money and you can use it as best as you can.

But like all policy options it is not a universal panacea. With money at stake local bargaining about the package may get tougher. Forcing people back into their homes can carry the same problems in individual cases. Worst of all will be the public's response when it is realised that it is hard to find care workers, affordable residential beds etc., i.e. when the problem of the supply side deficit is offloaded onto the most vulnerable in society.

Nevertheless in certain cases it will help. It may genuinely allow some family members the time to give social support themselves. In some parts of the country care workers are more readily available. Minority communities that have always looked after their own will welcome the cash. But the demand for assessment and care packages will grow as families undertaking their own social care claim a payment that will be more publicly available. Not only could it turn out to be a very costly system; there is the concern that families opting quickly for cash may not always be focusing upon the needs of the family member concerned: and who will be mother's advocate when the family have run off with the cash? Choice will bring a greater inequality again, and it is the poorest and most vulnerable who are likely to come off worst.

Finally in February 2003 the Health Service Ombudsman complicated this already complex process with the report on, "NHS Funding for Long Term Care". In four case studies the report argued that national guidance on NHS funding support for long term care was being applied too restrictively - although the national guidance document is itself somewhat of a Delphic oracle. If this leads the NHS into residential as well as nursing home use; or even into specialist domiciliary care for the chronically ill it would be beneficial for those patients. But if it led the NHS to cream off scarce resources from local authorities by bidding up prices due to the supply side deficit the general position of those requiring means tested social care could worsen. If the NHS is to be drawn down this road some rules are required and the first will be investment in new NHS long term care facilities. But there is little chance of this happening because the cost implications are out of reach given the major funding initiative in direct *health* care support.

7 Conclusion

This chapter has indicated that the growing supply side deficit in health, also exists in social care and that the latest figures on residential and nursing home beds show a 6% fall over the last four years. The industry also believes that numbers are continuing down. This is happening at a time when health is trying to cope with its own growing supply side pressures by taking tougher action on delayed discharges including fining local authorities for slow compliance. This in turn totally ignores the supply side problems that face social services and encourages inappropriate responses that will not benefit the client, but may bring some relief to delayed discharge numbers.

Against this background the chapter has charted the shift in government thinking, (and that of the House of Commons Select Committee), away from tackling the issue of residential and nursing home beds and towards more home based care packages with staff, equipment, adaptations and better use of patient monitoring by using modern technology. The government appears to be linking this change to the idea of direct cash payments (still *assessed* by social services), but giving clients greater choice in deciding what they need. The weaknesses of this were spelt out in the section above. Also, switching away from present levels of residential home dependence carries its own risks.

If the government is seen as placing less emphasis upon residential and nursing home beds and turning more to home care strategies there is no question that this will encourage a further decline in national supply; particularly at the lower cost end. If the government's apparent policy direction is to continue and succeed there is one consequence that appears to have been overlooked. With demographic change and a rising volume and proportion of frail elderly in the population, home care packages will tie up substantial housing stock in the public and private sector. These will typically be two and three bedroomed houses and the condition of this housing stock will almost certainly decline. At a time when the government is pressing for more housing and when local hostility to new building in the south of England is growing, is it wise to re-balance the distribution of social care? And if a policy mistake is recognised a few years down the line how easy will it be to tempt back the private and voluntary residential home providers? Yet again the government appears to be on the point of choosing a flawed policy option and it must be hoped that the rapid backtracking on the Social Care Act 2000 is the beginning of a recognition of fundamental policy errors; rather than merely a short tactical withdrawal.

Again, if the government continues to increase the focus upon home care packages we are likely to see a future in which the wealthier move to residential/nursing homes and the less wealthy die at home with their care package. Does this matter in a market economy? Will the public see social care in the same light as health care? If the two services are merged as the Select Committee almost advocated then the answer is likely to be 'yes'; but can any Chancellor afford the consequences?

As in health, what is required is a firm policy to tackle the supply side deficit within realistic growth assumptions. What is also necessary in social care is to recognise that health and social care are two separate systems that convey different 'rights' to patients and to clients and that they must operate separately within a required framework of collaboration. Attempts to 'merge' these services would do irreparable damage to both, because with merger it will become impossible to sustain means testing. General taxation cannot provide the answer because the extent of the qualitative rather than quantitative judgements involved in assessing clients will continue to erode cost control either at the expense of health spending, or of an increasingly unwilling taxpayer. The right way for the UK to reform is outlined in the following chapter.

CHAPTER 5

PROPOSAL FOR A DURABLE HEALTH CARE SYSTEM IN THE UK

The previous chapters have explained why New Labour's NHS is not sustainable despite a substantial cash injection and many initiatives that are individually helpful and necessary. This chapter outlines an alternative model that addresses the current dilemmas and which will have the durability to survive in future economic fluctuations. The chapter distinguishes between two strategic questions.

- What do we want to achieve? What is the framework for a durable health care system and what has to be done to achieve it?

- How do we respond to the immediate challenges and shortages in the shorter term, that appear to block progress to longer term objectives?

Government's response to the longer term question has been relatively unco-ordinated. There has been the Wanlass Report and its financial targets; lists of more of this and that, (usually staffing, equipment, etc), and better of the other, (usually clinical outcomes in designated services), and a great deal of teamwork and partnership; but frustratingly no overall framework within which to put these different pieces of the jigsaw. Ironically, this lack of a final focused picture of what the national health care system will become is contributing to the current lack of confidence among NHS staff.

For reasons already discussed the government's response to the shorter term questions looks gimmicky; increasingly seems to be a series of panic reactions, and its total dependence upon importing health care resource is clearly unsustainable to almost everyone who knows the NHS. The proposals in this chapter seek clarity of objectives and methodology; so before the durable health care system is outlined it is necessary to clarify some of the basic premises that form a framework for the system.

1 The Basic Premises

The list below is meant to be logically sequential rather than in any order of significance.

i NHS health care should be, "Free at the Point of Delivery"

The vast majority of health care is currently free at the point of delivery. Only those opting for private health care for some services (maximum 6%), and the means testing of certain dental, optical and prescription charges lie outside this free at the point of delivery principle. But there are also health provisions that simply lie outside the NHS. This includes purchased transplant organs, certain pharmaceuticals, and services that are simply not provided due to lack of health justification despite some social and individual pressures for inclusion.

This freedom at the point of delivery is embedded into the culture of the UK. It is not politically possible, nor in my view desirable, to remove this freedom. But the present boundaries of the NHS, illustrated above, are currently rather nebulous and certainly open-ended. There needs to be greater clarity about what this NHS does and about who receives NHS treatment. Neither of these clarifications would alter the basic concept of a health care system, free at the point of delivery.

ii Health Services should be, "Funded out of Taxation, and Borrowing"

For those of us who support a public health care system funded out of taxation, it is necessary to accept public borrowing, for years in which Exchequer revenue fluctuates downwards whilst NHS demand and expenditure rises. (The relevance of this is later in the chapter.) The reason for supporting this principle of funding out of taxation is again that it is culturally embedded in the UK and change is not politically feasible. The analogy of water, gas, telephones, etc, going into the private sector is a false one. The public always paid for water and gas etc, and continued to do so after the privatisation. Health care, since 1948, has always been free and all insurance alternatives involve some up-front payment that contributes to making them politically less achievable even though the culture of other European countries has grown around the acceptance of social insurance with up-front payment. For the record a largely or wholly payroll tax system would mostly alleviate this problem, but even if taxes fell to the point where take home pay was not affected, the negative aspects of any employer contribution (always a part of existing payroll systems), on UK competitiveness would be economically undesirable. Finally, to be clear, this rejection of an insurance based system is pragmatic. If anyone invented a system that made the UK population acquiescent, and which did not infringe upon the need for equality within a rationed service, it would be worthy of serious consideration.

iii The Secretary of State is Responsible for Public Health Provision

If one accepts that public health care will be funded by taxation one inescapable consequence is that the Secretary of State will be answerable in the House of Commons, not just for strategic issues,

119

but also for questions relating to the failures of the system in MPs' constituencies. This is because the adversarial nature of politics means that points will always be scored in the House and no Secretary of State could survive by simply saying, "I'm not responsible - ask the assistant sector manager in Slagthorpe", to a litany of horrors rehearsed for television and the press. Creating an NHS Corporation is always possible, but when the Secretary of State is under politically embarrassing pressure he will have to instruct it on the *specific* case: at which point it becomes a government department in all but name. Many Secretaries of State have dreamt about getting away from these embarrassing individual failings and most of the pressure for arms length corporations has come from this source. The NHS would like to be free of this constraint; my own political party and most current commentators the same, but it cannot free the Secretary of State from being answerable in the House, and having a department to support him. Whatever body/group exists with executive authority for the day to day management of health will have to be generally directed by and answerable to the Secretary of State, as long as the service is paid for out of *national* taxation.

iv Equality of Provision as a Fundamental Value

This issue is quite fundamental to the future of UK health care and is considered more fully now because of its importance to subsequent proposals. At one level the issue of choice in a free service should not arise. Everyone would wish to have the best of everything. Why would anyone *choose* to have an inferior service and to wait longer than clinically necessary. At another level those who advocate choice may mean an economist's choice; between alternative uses for a resource that is finite in the short term. The trouble with this 'choice' is that it has to be a choice to forgo something in order to have something else; the economics of the market. But as there is no consumer cost (price) why should I forgo anything? When politicians tell the public that they have choice

120

they (the politicians) are thinking of economic choice. Because health care is free at the point of delivery the public receives the message as: 'I can have whatever I like'. Making a PCT patients' forum decide *between* more community mental health or more stroke care services is a recipe for rancour and conflict. Chapter 1 illustrated the implications of the growth of single issue health politics and the effect of neighbouring PCTs making radically different choices.

At a further level there is widespread national recognition that the present NHS suffers a significant supply side deficit illustrated in Chapters 2 and 3. Giving choice in the face of such a supply/ demand imbalance is almost an insult to human intelligence. Rationing exists in almost every sector of the NHS and as it cannot be resolved by price it has to be resolved by delayed access; and by the day to day decisions of clinicians to diagnose and treat within budget.

The 'rationing' referred to here is at present partially unmanaged and certainly unacknowledged rationing. Politicians simply do not use the word and managers dare not use it. Failure to recognise it in public and failure to manage it openly can lead to damaging health consequences for individuals. There will *always* be a limit to what the State can provide in a free at the point of delivery health care system funded out of taxation. That limit will change according to GDP, the economic health of the nation, and supply availability. It could contract in adversity despite an overall long term expansion. The rationing limits on the health service should be well known and publicised: this is how long you can expect to wait until treatment; that is a service not available on the NHS; this service has priority, that does not. At present the services that are not really provided on the NHS are a mystery to the public; this Trust will do it, that one won't; this item you can wait forever to receive because it is not within the waiting list system; that item is

121

available, but only if you've passed tests so stringent that you may be too ill to benefit long term. (Women trying to obtain a DEXA scan for osteoporosis will understand this last example.) Today in the south east the standard ultrasound scanning of healthy pregnant women is less good than it was twenty years ago. Rationing by stealth is of no benefit to the public. **Rationing by delay and rationing by quality of provision needs to be known, so that effective action can be taken to achieve national equality of access on the basis of need.**

This 'choice' is not to be confused with the issue of 'packaging'. What colour we paint the surgery; how we arrange the chairs; which leaflets are printed to help patients; whether this consultant sees his outpatients in one place or another; how we organise booking and queuing in the blood clinic; how we resolve the parking problems, etc, are all packaging. These non-economic non-clinical decisions are all issues where the 'patient voice' is both relevant and helpful to service users. It is when local choice has an economic impact, eg community mental health *or* stroke care, that the local 'patient voice' is flawed because it will disempower specific patient groups in the community and undermine the principle of equality of provision which is the only basis on which rationing can survive in a democratic society. The famous 'Oregon experiment' of allowing the local community to choose public services by ballot has never caught on for both of these reasons.

To avoid misunderstanding this principle of equality cannot deliver *absolutely* equal quality. Six surgeons here will not produce identical quality with six surgeons there. The proper study of clinical outcomes and the knowledge of variations in outcomes will, however, work to avoid wide disparities. New service developments can be piloted and, if viable, placed within the rationing structure and funded to whatever nationally balanced provision is agreed. But those hostile to the public recognition of rationing and its permanence should not attack the idea with references to modest outcome variations, when the reality is ten surgeons here, four surgeons there coupled with gross disparities in access. Those of us who know the NHS can name the sink hospitals now - but millions of people have to use them. They are among the ones that won't be allowed to apply for Foundation Hospital status!

So this fourth basic premise is that a free at the point of delivery health care system funded out of taxation has to be based upon *genuine* equality of service to all citizens according to need; and that there should be no citizens who are 'more equal than others'.

v **Specialisation and Generalisation in Clinical Services**
Improving a health care service means improving clinical outcomes. All other objectives are subordinate to this one and in the end there are no real proxy measures other than *actual* clinical outcomes. Raising UK outcomes to the generality of other First World countries requires the increasingly sophisticated skills of the sub-specialist clinicians and modern 'sub-specialist' equipment and services to support them. The Royal College of Physicians is now beginning its switch from 'general physician on take', to acute medicine specialists and its recognition of the need for this is a milestone. The clinical staffing of acute hospitals has to be based upon this partnership of specialists within each of the broad clinical divisions of medicine. Nursing and other clinical professions also need to be able to apply this principle. At present the government is trying to enlarge generalism; eg a higher and higher proportion of non-consultant career grades; shorter time in SHO training; shorter time at specialist registrar level; inadequate priority for diagnostic services. All this while still demanding improved clinical outcomes. The two objectives are mutually exclusive: if improving clinical outcomes is a basic objective,

123

specialisation wins. None of this contradicts the need for good quality generalists at the first level of access to clinical services in the community and a degree of generalist backup to the consultant specialists' teams at hospital level.

As a postscript there is a somewhat callous opinion that intermediate procedures, and therefore patients, can all be left to less well trained generalists. They do an adequate job. Indeed if they focus more narrowly and undertake high volumes they can become very expert; but at this point they cease to be generalists and become 'specialists' at a lower level of clinical complexity. It is outcomes that matter and clinicians working within their sub-specialty are a necessary means to achieving those outcomes. If we apply the acid test of what we would want for our families and ourselves in hospital the answer is clear cut - the appropriate specialist consultant.

vi The Boundary between Health and Social Care

The state will never have the ability in the UK (in the foreseeable future) to fund social care as a free at the point of delivery service paid out of taxation. Not only is social care currently means tested, but also the bulk of national expenditure on social care is personal expenditure. Therefore there will always be a divide between health and social care: they are two fundamentally different systems. In social care the client pays some or all costs and therefore can and should be free to *choose*. These two systems need to be managed separately and therefore the challenge is to ensure that the interface works as smoothly and efficiently as possible.

At present the government is making ad hoc sallies across this divide by selecting social care services to fund. The reasoning for this seems mixed. The new system of funding up to six weeks of intermediate care after hospital discharge plus any equipment requirements is beneficial to the existing health system and to the client and will help the interface to work more smoothly. The offer to pay a certain amount towards nursing care in nursing homes was a PR gimmick that has been positively harmful at the interface because of widespread public misunderstanding of what has turned out to be little more than a gesture as far as the *total* cost of a nursing home is concerned. The boundary between health and social care needs to be crystal clear and easy to understand and in the main ad hoc 'freebies' across the divide simply cause the system to become confused; even to those working in it. Government can, of course, decide to make particular services totally free at the point of delivery if it has the long term revenue; but these should be at the interface; should transfer to health or joint management; and should leave the new boundary between free and means-tested services equally simple and easy for the public to understand. A single management of these services in Northern Ireland has not clarified these issues in the minds of the public and has not eliminated the professional tensions that exist across the interface despite having much lower volumes of client payment than the UK average.

These six basic premises create a framework for the detail that follows. Inevitably they all involve value judgements; often not the most popular judgements. But the health care system that is outlined below is logically consistent with this framework and has the capacity to be durable if these premises are accepted.

There was a choice as to how to answer the two questions at the opening of the chapter. What do we want to achieve and how do we respond to the current short term pressures. We could regard them as two separate sections; and go over the list of issues twice; once for each question. Or we could describe each issue/proposal once and handle both questions under each heading. The latter approach has been chosen as more logical and certainly more readable.

2 A Hospital and Community Health Care System fit for the Purpose

The model set out opposite illustrates a necessary set of relationships between the providers of health and social care within a simplified NHS structure. Each element of the model is then explained and analysed in more detail.

FIG I
Health and Social Service Provider Relationships with GPs involved as Independent Contractors of Service

FIG II
Health and Social Service Provider Relationships with GPs involved as salaried employees of Community Services Trusts

⟷ = patient/client flows between providers (this diagram does not illustrate major variations in the volume of patient/client flows eg relatively very low between acute hospital trusts and mental health trusts and very significant between GPs and acute hospital trusts).

Acute Hospital Trusts

Acute hospital trusts need to provide acute and elective medical and surgical services on a single site (two closely adjacent linked sites may be manageable, but are not ideal). These trusts will require several decentralised support facilities covering diagnostics, many outpatient services, day case surgery and sometimes more specialised day facilities, but they will not require acute overnight beds of any type. These decentralised facilities will be within the main population centres; they may be attached to Community Services Trust centres or self-standing. No other services (including non-acute beds) should be included within the acute hospital trusts.

The most crucial questions about these trusts is 'how many' and 'where'. The starting point is the analysis done by the Surgeons' and Physicians' Royal Colleges and the BMA. The original Surgeon's proposition of a 450,000-500,000 population base outlined in Chapter 2 is today even more compelling than when originally proposed in 1996. The emphasis upon improving outcomes; the need to switch increasingly from generalist to specialist hospital services to achieve this; the urgent necessity to maintain strong clinical teams against a background of labour shortage; the importance of treating acutely ill patients on sites possessing the flexibility to respond quickly to complex conditions all lead to this one conclusion. Furthermore, without this population base many disease conditions do not occur in sufficient volume to enable clinical skills to be maintained and to support a 24 hours, seven days a week service.

In 1996 it was claimed that this population base could provide *every* acute hospital with all surgical services up to and including a full vascular service. It would also provide consultant teams in virtually all the medical specialties and would provide a base for the development of acute medicine, as a specialty in its own right, growing to replace 'the general physician on take'. Inevitably there are highly specialised services that do not fit this pattern and where

128

national provision is more limited due to small demand. Certain acute hospital trusts would be designated providers, just as some are designated teaching hospitals. Where this is the case such sub-specialties should be regionally balanced and where possible national super-specialties should avoid being clustered in one part of the UK.

The requirement for acute and elective beds; and for theatre, clinic and diagnostic facilities should be determined by a national team involving representative senior clinical input which should prioritise within a government agreed resource framework. With a half million population the basic service requirement should be identical, but weighted for morbidity factors; then varied by the resource requirement for the more limited specialist services; and by a new and more realistic assessment of the resource required for teaching.

There are two sides to this more controversial proposal: on one side a high quality clinical service focused on high value outcomes; on the other side a miscellany of objections. There is a generalised dislike of the inconvenience of greater distance. There are those who object to the extra time needed for public transport and/or the cost of private transport (including those unable to pay privately). There are those who do not trust placing greater reliance upon an enhanced ambulance service. There are those 10/15% of the UK population who *would* be too far from the acute hospital with a half million population base. There are those who would fudge the issue by sending one clinical care pathway in one direction and another in the opposite direction so that every town hospital can keep a little bit of something.

There is really no contest. A high quality clinical service focusing on high value outcomes has to prevail, because all the objections can be met except for the issue of some extra personal time in travelling. Ensuring affordable access has to be taken seriously and has to be established at the *start* of any change. The 10/15% sparse populations will require to continue using old style acute hospitals. Their limitations, as now, are a recognised cost of choosing to live in a sparsely populated area of the UK. The civic pride that leads to so many bitter contests over siting cannot be allowed to diminish health quality, but it should be turned more positively, to working in partnership over matters as sensitive as hospital locations and titles etc. In the 1990s all the most bitter hospital merger conflicts I have been involved with had at their core the fact that *we* (our town, community etc) are better than *them*; or that our service is currently *better* than theirs and we want to keep it so. No morally responsible government should shirk facing up to these minority challenges: improved clinical outcomes within a free at the point of delivery service equally available to all must win the debate; if not we swing back to inequality and the market.

On present population this policy might only allow for around 130 such acute hospitals (or paired adjacent site hospitals) in the whole UK, but areas of sparse population require the maintenance of some traditional acute services so that perhaps 150 acute hospitals would be needed. If so the 80% of current population that live within *five* miles of an acute hospital would eventually live within *eight* miles of an acute hospital when the new acute hospital configuration was established.

Public response to these proposals will be strongly negative in the first instance; and no government likes to be unpopular. Even so the present government showed signs of continuing to accept gradual change in this direction until February 2003 when their new guidance on service configuration gave local communities an effective right to block change; which they will always do. This surrender to the status quo lobby constitutes an appalling abandonment of leadership which they must know will have negative consequences for public health.

The challenge in this chapter is that the twelve years of policy by stealth must come to an end, there should be a clearly stated national policy and the government should *lead*. They should do this by taking the debate and the reasoning to the public with full clinical support; because the present totally stalled progress on hospital rationalisation has to be re-vitalised. If this is not done the worsening labour supply deficit will speed up the quality crisis in the many smaller acute hospitals before a modern acute hospital structure is in place. This deficit is not the *reason* for making the change; it is merely the reason why a very leisurely incremental progress is not now an option; as Labour could find out to its cost in the next two to three years. The government simply cannot survive if it allows the understandings and prejudices of the general public to remain so at odds with the reality that is known and understood by most health care professionals and government policy makers. It is time for a Pericles not a Kleon!

The scope of this book does not allow a detailed description and analysis of how this acute hospital modernisation programme will be structured and introduced, but it is necessary to consider a few key facets of the change.

- Equality of access and service requires a geographically balanced national pace of implementation for which PFI is uniquely unsuitable, because of its inherently cherry-picking approach.

- The under-provision of acute medical beds, which has bedevilled many early PFI hospitals has to be rectified. The implications of demographic change are still not being factored into the calculation. In a few cases this might mean creating capacity beyond current staffing ability.

- City hospital site mergers and new build are easier to understand even if they have their own particular difficulties. Outside the metropolitan areas mergers will more frequently involve two towns and adjoining communities. The initiative is more likely to fail if an either/or, winner and loser approach is adopted. Town centres are *not* the best locations for acute hospitals. In the North Hertfordshire example in Chapter 2 Stevenage and Welwyn Garden City should adopt a site half way between them where land transferred from Green Belt can ensure building and car parking space. Each town would still be a location for many decentralised acute hospital services, see page 138 of this chapter, but not acute hospital beds.

- These changes should go hand-in-hand with further investment in emergency ambulance services, and non-emergency public transport and/or taxi voucher systems.

- Acute hospitals and sites that remain within the new structure will need to expand and greater car parking space, if necessary by multistorey building, will be essential. This issue of parking is not an unbalanced obsession, but it is vital to secure longer term public acceptance.

- As indicated PFI must be abandoned in place of public build Treasury funding. The present PFI is too expensive, the financial structure has forced unacceptable restrictions on service provision, the short life span required by contract is frightening and PFI just cannot cope with the size of the building programme required. These must be NHS owned hospitals.

Financing Hospital Building: A New Approach

Fifty new hospitals at £600 million costs £30 billion; adaptations to other sites could cost another £10 billion. £40 billion over ten years would not be acceptable, perhaps, to a prudent Chancellor, but there are other ways. PFI schemes originally had to generate 6% out of Trust revenue as "savings" to pay for the PFI facility. This is well above current interest rates and is likely to remain so for some long time. $3^1/2$% War Loan is unredeemable government stock raised by public subscription in a time of national emergency. At present prices 4% Health Loan Stock that was eventually redeemable would allow the public to support the programme at a reasonable guaranteed rate of return.

The first objection is that the public would not buy in at this capital volume even over ten years. One important inducement could involve pensions. At present the law allows a 25% cash lump sum to be taken by owners of private pensions but requires that at age 75 the remaining 75% of the pension *must* be taken as an annuity if this has not already happened. If pensioners were allowed to take a further 25% tax free, provided it was invested in 4% Health Loan stock, the attractiveness of the fund would be substantial. The Chancellor would tax the 4% income; he would not lose this tax revenue on the transaction and pensioners preferring cash could sell out on the open market. Alternatively if the Chancellor felt this would make other public borrowing more expensive, pensioners using this facility could be required to hold the stock for a minimum number of years to qualify for the tax free incentive.

It might also be objected that this initiative would increase the State's share of the national economy and the volume of public borrowing and public debt beyond prudent levels and that this might to some extent damage the growth capacity of the economy. One interesting way of dealing with this would be to require government to ring fence the remaining 2% (if the NHS has to pay a 'notional' return of 6%) and to use it exclusively to buy back 4% Health Loan on the open market. If interest rates remain static this could take 50 years to complete, but it gives government both a guaranteed source of income (6% as a first charge on NHS revenue) and a certainty of the eventual elimination of the debt. Market sentiment would be much more positive to a self-eliminating debt than to purely unredeemable stock and would also respond positively to the economic implications of a building boom just as private sector commercial building was rapidly slowing. Recent government changes to this required 6% rate of return are merely to do with making PFI more attractive. Internally there is no need to reduce it if PFI constraints are removed.

A further objection concerns the ability of a Trust paying 6% 'savings' to take on the additional responsibility of building repair and maintenance borne by PFI owners under that model. There are three elements to the response.

- As government 'redeems' the debt by buying back the loans it reduces the 6% savings requirements by a fractional annual adjustment. Eventually, Trust by Trust, this will eliminate the 6%; but this of itself is not enough.

- Government will achieve capital sales from this hospital modernisation programme. If the only charge on this capital is land purchase for new building then a separate *national* capital account could be set up to ring fence this money and use it (interest and capital) to provide maintenance and repair support to Trusts on a national formula.

- At present government is pushing revenue to Trusts faster than some can reasonably use it. To avoid distorted spending patterns Trusts should be treated like schools and allowed to hold revenue, along with any general underspends, so that longer term repair and maintenance costs can be covered.

None of these is sufficient in itself, but together they form a realistic set of sources to cover necessary Trust expenditure on sustaining their hospital stock. They also squash the notion that particularly valuable land belongs to one Trust on a lottery jackpot basis. The opening assumption of equality of access and service must mean that all assets belong equally to all the population. This also means that Foundation Trusts, as a uniquely anti-egalitarian concept, are no part of a new NHS. Their very existence will widen the quality gap between them and the sink hospital trusts from day one. They will take their best staff and cream off some of their revenue flows. How in these conditions can a sink hospital ever be expected to 'catch up' and earn their own Foundation status? Eventually we would be told sink hospitals are as they are because patients *'choose'* to go elsewhere.

Community Services Trusts (CSTs) and GP services

As providers these Trusts can be seen as expanded Primary Care Trusts (PCTs) but without the purchaser/contractor role. GP practices could opt to be within these Trusts and managed by them or external to the Trusts as independent contractors. The rationale for this is developed later in the Chapter. The service boundaries of CSTs should be the same across the UK. All non-acute NHS services apart from mental health should be managed in CSTs. All general non-acute beds; the physically disabled, learning disability services still within health and all traditional community services (with the exception of community midwifery) constitute the provision proposed for CSTs.

Mental Health Trusts (MHTs)

The boundary with Mental Health Trusts (MHTs) seems clear, with learning disability provision primarily in Social Services, but there is an issue with respect to dementia and the elderly mentally ill (EMI). Clinical treatment is the responsibility of the NHS and where this requires an NHS setting (acute or otherwise) it is the responsibility of the MHT. The problem is lack of sufficient residential care settings for clients with moderate to severe dementia (who are not EMI clinically diagnosed patients) and the number of such patients/clients is expected to grow. Given the same means-testing interface between MHTs and social services authorities as outlined in Chapter 4 they could develop as Mental Health Partnership Trusts which are increasing in number. A more formal expansion of partnerships is to be supported.

GP Services

Finally, if GPs decide to work within CHTs they will be salaried employees who work with, but do not employ, their clinical and other colleagues in the community. National contracts must give them the protection of maximum list sizes. For GP practices that opt for independent contractor status the contract income should be volume sensitive and related to direct GP service provision. This should include formula running costs for those staff, including professional staff, directly employed and non-staff costs to provide contracted services to the CSTs. The reason for this option is explained in the staffing section below.

Social Services

There should be a new boundary between health and social services. The dividing line between the NHS and local government in the provision of health and social care should be that all fully free services should be within CSTs, and all means-tested services should remain with local government. This makes the principle of potential user payment the point of interface and one which may change over time. If ever government wished to extend freedom from payment it must therefore bring the service and its costs within *national* provision. If it wishes to diminish the range of State funding it would put services back into *local government* provision.

It is proposed here that the first six weeks of social care in whatever setting should be fully funded irrespective of means and be provided by CSTs. This means that *all* step down options to facilitate acute hospital discharge are managed by one agency, the CST, to ensure more speedy and effective patient transfer. During the six weeks it will be the responsibility of social service departments to assess and arrange longer term means-tested social care and local government will automatically pick up all responsibilities at six weeks. This will still require close liaison and partnership between CSTs and local authorities to ensure the best options for clients. It also means that the *hospital* social work team (in the CST) will work as one, securing the best options on discharge for all patients irrespective of address and will work with hospital social workers in other Trusts where necessary; whilst local government will employ the community social

136

workers. In the case of OTs immediate equipment and aides will be the responsibility of the CST team, whilst long term assessment for building adaptations will rest with local government OTs as well as all post-six week support. This pattern of provision makes the Chancellor's proposed re-imbursement charges unnecessary. Once the issue of means-testing is taken away from the point of discharge, lack of CST staff or residential/nursing home beds would be the only causes of delay.

The consequences of this 'limited' six weeks proposal are far reaching. Acute hospital trusts and social services departments would have no direct contact or dealings with one another. Managing the transfer home of clients needing domiciliary packages, including assessment of the home environment, would rest with hospital discharge social workers wholly and exclusively employed by CSTs. The same would apply to managing the transfer to Nursing Home or Residential accommodation. Finally all community social work staff would stay with local government, responsible for the maintenance of longer term, means tested social provision and the support of 'step up' provision with and alongside the CSTs.

3 A Public Health Care System

Who Are the Purchasers?
The purchaser of NHS health care is the government, which purchases on behalf of taxpayers. This is inevitable in a free at the point of delivery service paid out of general taxation; it was as true in 1991 as it is today. So what has the "purchaser/commissioner" initiative of the last decade been about? All governments are anxious to ensure the most effective and efficient use of public resources to maximise health gain from health investment. Giving the NHS financial allocation to new purchaser health authorities and GP fundholders in 1991 was an innovative means of trying to ensure this health gain. But in 1991 the straightforward application of the

performance measurement and performance management (PMM) tools that are central to the running of large commercial organisations was not possible in the NHS. Counting deaths, discharges and waiting lists is as far as the NHS ever got in forty years. Körner statistics were beginning to make an impact on measurement, but performance management was, to be charitable, in its infancy. In 1991 'purchasing' was the only *immediately* available tool that could offer some prospect of affecting performance and the government was right to take it. But the anxieties about spawning a whole new bureaucracy proved justified.

Today there are two choices not one. In ten years NHS performance measurement and performance management has improved substantially and is one positive legacy of the last five years, even though the task is not finished and the national computer record continues to prove elusive. But it is now becoming sufficient as a tool to monitor performance against targets. The efficient collection of meaningful data, at the appropriate time to guide service development and direction, is essential and is here to stay. The government may well have done this in an insensitive and burdensome way, and we must learn from early mistakes and reduce pressure on clinical staff, but it was essential for them to have started the process and they deserve that credit. But we now have two separate and overlapping tools; 'purchasing/commissioning'; and performance measurement and management (PMM); each carrying its own bureaucracy and costs. This leads me to a very simple but controversial conclusion. The NHS does not need two systems, two bureaucracies and two sets of costs: indeed each system gets in the way of the other and confuses rather than supports effective action. Purchasing was the only available tool at the time, but now there is a performance framework for focusing upon and driving health benefit per pound invested. The whole purchasing/commissioning framework should now be dismantled, but all Trusts should continue to deliver key strategic PMM targets against investment. This raises a whole series of issues and concerns.

- The system of performance measurement has flaws; is not yet equally comprehensive across all clinical services and is still capable of local manipulation. This is true, but if the central role of PMM is recognised as the measure and motivator of health gain through higher productivity its development will be even more rapid and the released costs from purchasing/ commissioning will support that development.

- Health outputs are not the same as health outcomes and if genuine health gain is the goal we are still poor at PMM in outcomes. Again, the NHS has made progress in the last five years. From death/discharge data to re-admissions and now the start on replacement/repair data is a framework on which to build; but, yes, health status data post treatment is still limited, intermittent and largely research based. It will need investment.

- The end of purchasing/commissioning does not mean uncontrolled freedom for GPs. Their prescribing; clinical referral and the output performance of teams (whether in CSTs or independent contractor services) will be subject to PMM (with targets) in the same way as Trusts. But, importantly, they will not have to refuse to refer a patient to hospital on budgetary grounds. PMM will make them justify the referral clinically, but will never refuse the right to refer. As a result, a necessarily more sophisticated waiting list measurement will help to identify the true volume of demand; which data is vital if we are to achieve real health benefit.

- So who would establish, direct and monitor PMM? An NHS Management Board with executive functions should be empowered by Statute to carry out this function and make publicly available its performance measurement data. It should do this within a specific ring fenced annual budget voted by parliament as part of health funding. The Board should be answerable to parliament through Ministers for PMM. In one important issue of performance measurement the Board will be independent of Ministers. Government can fund and require particular data sets, but they will lose the general right to control the publication of data, (or to avoid the collection of particular data), as part of greater accountability and transparency in public services.

The Board would also be responsible for the allocation of the health resources to Trusts and GP contractors; and for the management of the NHS as a whole. To do this it will require Regional Management; and Trust accountability will be through the Regions. Finally, in a service as unique as the NHS, with strong political leadership, the Leeds location was always a major mistake to the detriment of the NHS national executive in fulfilling its role. Indeed it encouraged the development of a surrogate 'executive' of advisers in Whitehall. The NHS Management Board should function from within Whitehall; bean counting can be done anywhere.

Resource Allocation

After fifty years of failing to achieve equitable resource allocation in the UK radical change is required. Each Regional annual allocation should be based upon just two funding streams. The first is to be calculated on population by weighted age group collected annually *from patient registration data from GP practices*. The second is to be based upon clinical referral and treatment data by disease category; going no further than this in the direction of morbidity data. Only supra-Regional services will be centrally resourced by the Management Board. When established, the transfer from the old to the new funding formula should take place within three years despite this being a challenging target. These same principles will apply to the Regional funding of community service and mental health trusts.

Of itself this system does not secure equality. For this reason all Regions shall provide the same range of Regional services just as all acute hospital Trusts will provide the same range of clinical services per half million or so population. In the same way that the Management Board will determine the location and funding of supra-regional services Regions will fund and determine the location of a nationally agreed list of specialist Regional services. These moves will include a re-balancing of the provision of teaching trusts to ensure a far better geographic balance of teaching resource and expertise. Public consultation, maximum patient access and clinical supply are all elements in these decisions. Where this entails new service developments in traditionally under-resourced Regions this will be pump-primed for a fixed period of years after which funding will depend only upon the national formula.

The final radical step is the basing of funding upon GP patient registrations referred to above. The medical card and number should again become the key to NHS care that it was originally (with or without the electronic identification that most of us would like). Many of the most disadvantaged UK citizens get a poor health service by failing to be registered with a GP. Compelling registration and re-establishing it, if necessary, every time citizens present in hospital as an acute patient, is to their benefit and is a social responsibility. (But this is not to suggest that people should have compulsory general health care if they wish to refuse it.)

There is another reason for the medical card. The UK has many illegal immigrants and unentitled health tourists. London alone has over half a million illegal immigrants. They all receive free health care from hospitals and to a lesser extent from other services, such as mental health. At present Greater London is under-funded for this reason. Government should do one of two things; it should either debar illegal immigrants from free NHS care, or it should openly count 'illegal' patients and directly fund the Trusts on a fee for item of service basis. I would be content with the latter option; it enables fairer funding, it prevents UK patients suffering poorer resource provision (where the demand is as high as London), it forces government to be honest about the extent of illegal immigration, and it creates a basis for tackling health tourism which is fast becoming a burden that the NHS cannot manage. Tragic perhaps; but those who are simply health tourists and who get free treatment due to the current lack of identity controls should be debarred from NHS provision by withdrawing current rules and guarantees.

Government also needs a mechanism to handle those who claim refugee or economic migrant status *primarily* to achieve treatment for a serious disease condition. Medical checks should be compulsory for at least the major conditions that bring health tourists to the UK. If the government collected and disclosed the nationality and UK status of every person receiving NHS treatment on a particular day in Greater London the political consequences would be dramatic. But why should Londoners bear the cost?

Under PMM all health staff should code a service provided (in GP clinics, the community or in hospital) to a named patient *with* a medical number. There will also have to be a national list of allowed clinical and other services available within the public health care system. Requested services outside that list would be charged for at economic cost. To begin with, virtually all current NHS activities will be within the list. It will be important, however, from the outset, to have a list of obvious exclusions so that all *new* services and drugs, etc, can be considered before ad hoc entrepreneurial supply begins with one or two clinicians. Bureaucratic it is, but this type of exponential growth has undermined the resources and ultimately the provision and quality of core services for too long. Obvious candidates for omission have been well known for a long time and are rarely supplied; such as tattoo removal, cosmetic varicose veins, reversal of vasectomy etc. But there are more serious issues. Fertility treatment costs are very high and growing fast - but for women who already have healthy children!! Finally, there should be a standard

A&E department charge for all patients treated with a non-urgent condition judged to be appropriate to a GP service, with the option at triage of voluntarily going to the GP instead. Many patients today are turned away for this reason; but many are not and the option to charge and treat or refuse should be left to A&E staff operating national access criteria. The object is not the money, it is to reinforce what might be left of a sense of public responsibility for a public service.

4 Responding to the Labour Shortage

So far some readers may feel that the previous 'recommendations' for a new NHS are merely harking back to an earlier 'golden age' of the old NHS. This would be an unfair response. A five to ten year agenda to achieve an equalisation of NHS facilities and resources led by a major new, public, acute hospital building programme is exceptionally radical. It is something the old NHS never achieved in fifty years. Even when the capital is available it requires the political will to oppose strong local support for inequality.

Despite all this, it is true that my most significant and radical proposals are not the acute hospital building programme. They are in this section of the Chapter in the response to the labour shortage in health care.

In the UK today we are very short of doctors, nurses, teachers, policemen, allied health professionals, plumbers, carpenters, electricians, engineers, social workers, bricklayers and home care assistants. In response our educational system produces media studies graduates, lawyers and hairdressers. It does not need great intelligence to realise that education policy has failed the nation for several decades. The Conservative reliance upon laissez-faire is as much to blame as Labour's determination that half of all 21 year olds will be university graduates with all the expectations that went with that status when only 10% were graduates. Their mothers love it, and it may keep getting Labour re-elected, but at the cost of substantial and ultimately irreversible damage to the structure of the economy. National education policy and national manpower planning have been treated as if they are totally separate and unrelated activities. Until policy reflects properly the objectives of both there is no possibility of achieving radical structural reform. Fortunately this book is only concerned with the health segment of these policies.

The shortage of qualified staff in the NHS is overwhelmingly the greatest single cause of the failure of New Labour's reformed NHS to deliver improvements that the public can see. The negative effects of this shortage have also been compounded by government's policy initiatives. They are trying to maintain and improve labour supply whilst at the same time tearing apart the professional structure of the system in a battle which is being fought primarily with the medical profession, but which will ultimately damage all the clinical professions. They are trying to reverse the development of sub-specialism in medicine which alone can deliver the claimed goal of improved outcomes. Switching to shorter medical training; increasing the proportion of generalists; abandoning the required scientific background for medical training; strengthening the managerial agenda in clinical decision making all represent the abandonment of the greatest clinical strengths in the UK's international health reputation. This can only *damage* medical supply in the long term by demoralising those now working in the NHS and discouraging the abler scientists from looking to medicine as a long term and full time career. The short term palliative of mass importation of labour, to punish the doctors for their 'resistance', is no long term remedy and cannot reproduce and maintain the quality standards and health outcomes already achieved.

The proposals set out below focus *solely* upon how to achieve a long term rise in clinical labour supply within the UK in a way that builds upon the existing strengths of the UK professions. They seek to achieve success in the shortest possible time by adopting two

144

strategies. The first is to create *options* or choices in contracts to maximise the attractiveness of health employment. The second is to recognise that those best qualified to understand how to increase health outputs and health quality are those who spend their lives providing health care and that they should be offered the opportunity and independence, should they wish it, to use their skills properly. In the short term we must encourage staff to stay on; to work more hours and to be as near to full time as possible; but without offending those who really do not want to respond. We have to win again the affection and commitment towards the NHS that will restore morale.

To give effect to these strategies there would be a number of changes to national contracts affecting all staff.

i Hours of Work

The standard weekly hours of work for all staff would still be determined nationally, but its only relevance would be in determining how many hours (or medical sessions) are to be paid at standard rates. Thereafter each employee may agree any personal hours of work per week or month, and the time when they will be worked, which may include flexitime arrangements. This would be done at the time of employment and thereafter hours would only change by mutual agreement, or if the employer made certain working practices redundant, or if the employee gave six months notice of a reduction in weekly hours. All employees would then have a contract specifying the number of hours worked per week paid at a standard rate followed by an escalating rate for greater hours with a possible upper limit no lower than 72 hours per week. The escalator could be in four hour units with an hourly rate of at least double pay after twelve hours and pro rata upwards. None of this would prevent ad hoc voluntary overtime outside the personal hours contract, when mutually agreed and paid at the same escalator once hours exceeded national standard weekly hours.

145

The careful reader will note that these changes in hours give rights to employees rather than obligations. It creates new options for staff to fix their own working hours above or below the national standard and offers attractive remuneration and incentive for those able to offer more to the NHS.

This arrangement would require the partial suspension of the EU Working Time Directive and this should be done for a fixed period of time, specifically for health workers to deal with a national labour supply crisis. The government should set out its target for staffing to determine the future timing of the removal of the partial suspension; and the UK's willingness to import qualified EU trained doctors should argue strongly for the appropriateness of this emergency measure. Trainee doctors and those providing 'out of hours' services are the only groups of staff for whom this move would be significant. The removal of the August 1st 2004 deadline is *essential* to avoid the collapse of small and medium sized acute trusts.

There is a conspiracy theory that the government will press ahead with the Directive knowing that the collapse of the smaller acute hospitals will force acute hospital rationalisation. And that their alibi will be their apparent climbdown on hospital rationalisation in February 2003 when they made it subject to local approval. All we can do is wait and see.

ii A Salary Only Contract

The option of salary only contracts, but within PAYE regulations, would be primarily beneficial for shorter term employees either as a fixed term contract, or an open contract, with the employee option of giving notice of absence unpaid, eg for holidays. Ill health absence rules within the standard contract would apply, but would not carry payment. All benefits including pension would be part of salary, together with a cash equivalent of the local

146

absenteeism 'rate' based upon all non-holiday/non-training absences. Trusts would be required to calculate this annually in arrears. Using this contract the NHS would actively seek to reduce agency working.

iii A Self Employment Contract

Over twenty years the NHS has experienced privatisation in the form of out-sourcing mainly ancillary services to private companies 'so that the NHS could focus on its key role of clinical services to patients'. Many of these arrangements have been successful economically, but their main characteristic has been to lower the pay and conditions of those who do the work in exchange for profitability for private companies. Unfortunately, in the short term this option for achieving greater productivity will have to stay and there should be no bar to its extension into all branches of public health care. However, staff need a third option which allows them to take more control over their work and income. There should be a *voluntary* option of a self-employment contract individually, (or collectively through a partnership). There are far more opportunities for this than might first seem apparent, but these opportunities vary in different parts of the health service. The NHS has many experienced porters and cleaning supervisors who *could* take charge of a hospital service, recruit to a high standard and be remunerated for it. They should be allowed to go for it. These freedoms are not just about doctors fee for item of service!

Core contracts for self-employment would include:

a) A framework of broad quality standards, Trust supervision of delivery and mechanisms for requiring change.

b) Timeliness of delivery.

c) Participation in Trust procedures, eg audit.

d) Maintenance of professional skills etc.

e) Health and safety, data and data protection.

Labour only contracts means that the NHS would continue to supply capital (including space) consumables, maintenance and repair. Contracts would have to cover these issues and protect NHS interests, eg an agreed percentage of film failure in radiography etc, with gains or penalties to a partnership.

The principles above can be applied to many parts of the NHS. Some examples are quoted here. A partnership of midwives and support workers could take responsibility for a town or specific locality paid by the number of deliveries; maintaining specified ante-natal support, conducting the delivery (with or without medical assistance) and providing a limited list of post-natal support prior to handing over to the CST at a specified time. With the present average of deliveries per WTE midwife little above 20 p.a. there are those midwives who believe twice that number would be possible in a partnership; even one with rigorous perinatal and postnatal standards. If this is true the immediate remuneration implications for midwives would be impressive.

Pathology and radiology partnerships may or may not include medical staff as a matter of choice. They may be based on a whole hospital service or a department or defined specialist service. Quantity must be measured by demand, ie the request not the test and this requires weighting. The private sector already has robust and relatively simple ways of doing this. It would encourage Trusts to establish good demand management systems and increase their commitment to more sophisticated comparative performance measurement.

Doctors are always thought of first in the context of self-employment and this illustration has to be a little more detailed. To meet the premise of working *with* the profession and to maximise voluntary supply there should in future be two medical contracts on offer to consultants and GPs with doctors free to move between them without penalty during their career. As indicated in Chapter 4

GPs would have either a salaried contract with the CST or an independent practitioner contract. For consultants the choice would be between a salaried contract and a self-employment contract that would be work sensitive. Everyone who wishes should be entitled to try to maximise income by middle age and the private sector should not be the only option for workaholics.

Consultants worked a ten session contract that formally required a 35 hour working week with most consultants doing much more. This is now proposed for change in a new consultant contract of 40 hours per week. Not a good deal for patients if, as seems likely, it leads to a clocking on and clocking off mentality. (And why should the working week for doctors be higher than for every other salaried clinician?) In the Government's failed contract the sessional unit was rejected. But in the new system discussed here it would be re-introduced.

Partnership or self-employed consultants would contract, individually or collectively with the Trust for the provision of services. These contracts could require fixed four hour sessions with a fixed price for training sessions; medical audit sessions; and timed attendance for acute patient sessions. Thereafter clinical procedures would be individually priced within specialties.

The reader should be aware that self employment contracts will not come about quickly, even if selected service based pro-forma guidance contracts are set up nationally. There will be value in piloting contracts in different specialties and sub-specialties and the NHS Management Board may sub-contract a pro-forma contract and pilot to a specific Trust where there is a positive staff response.

Not all areas of health employment lend themselves equally to such an innovation, but the approach outlined here will allow the more entrepreneurial staff to get pilot schemes launched.

For the Trust a key benefit to achieve is greater productivity, not more cost for current productivity.

Medical consultant employment does not lend itself easily to this approach in all specialities; not even in all surgery and anaesthetics, but the opportunity to be innovative will lead to pilots that can then be developed and extended. Perhaps radiology and pathology lend themselves most easily to self-employment opportunities, particularly traditional radiology and histopathology where individuals can extend their working day ad hoc with fewer implications for other staff.

iv Training

Training issues are specific to each clinical profession and some key groups are considered below.

Doctors

There is a 'national' rate of growth in fully trained UK GPs and consultants that can be sustained in the longer term if resources are there to support it. This rate is at, or only slightly above, the 5% achieved by Kenneth Calman. The fact that his actual average was over 6% benefited from the transition to SpR training as a one off pump priming. This gross growth rate offers a net growth possibility of $3^1/2$% to 4% if doctors commit themselves to a lifetime of medicine as in the past. The long term lack of increase in the proportion of scientists produced by our educational system; the need to train properly with an ever expanding body of knowledge; and the need to balance trained resources between teaching, research and clinical practice *prevent* this natural rate of growth rising further and so far those who have sought to fight against this premise have achieved damage rather than benefit.

To recruit the necessary number of scientists (in the broader sense) into medical undergraduate training requires emergency measures.

- All medical undergraduate programmes should be free of charge and there should be a maintenance grant in exchange for three years equivalent work in the NHS after the completion of specialist training in hospital or general practice. The decision not to practise medicine in the NHS would require repayment with a fixed annual interest. This proposal would do more for social inclusion than all the government's discrimination schemes.

- Postgraduate training numbers would be based upon the 5% gross growth rate with some rebalancing between the specialties to cope with extreme needs like radiology. Consultant time required to provide training would be set nationally and would be ring-fenced in each contract. This would include time to train trainers so that eventually Medical Royal Colleges could not debar hospitals from training on grounds of inadequate capacity; and the new structure of acute trusts would anyway make this concern obsolete.

- The EU Working Time Directive's temporary suspension would allow a 72 hour on call contract for trainee doctors over the next ten years to deal with the crisis in medical supply but would not *require* it in all circumstances. The Department of Health would have to pay well for the work beyond 58 hours and part time training would be an automatic right requested after appointment. (Part time training posts are now openly offered, and training periods would be pro rata to hours worked.)

- Academic medicine is in supply crisis. The old income lead for academic medicine has to be restored in a modern way (as always inclusive of private practice income comparisons), research time has to be protected, and a new government research fund limited to those who teach undergraduate and postgraduate students in universities needs to be established with realistic funding levels.

- For those higher specialties at Regional or supra Regional level six full years of specialist registrar training and practice will be essential.

- Medical supply has been badly affected by the relatively recent sudden switch from male to female entrants to medical training. If this continues medical supply could decline due to the perfectly proper exercise of the right to work part time. During the initial ten years 'the system' should attempt to ensure a minimum core level of male entrants. With free undergraduate training a strong commitment to longer term NHS employment is a legitimate issue in selection.

In an ideal world there should be a widespread political consensus to establish and maintain this structure followed by a review of progress over a ten year period.

- Postscript on Medical Private Practice
  Medical private practice cannot be stopped. It is, rightly, a part of the national market in professional services that gives access via money to some of the best lawyers, architects, doctors etc. To introduce a ban on NHS doctors working in private practice merely serves to drive out those highly gifted people whose competence has caused them to rise to the top of their field; and further discourages potential doctors who end up in other fields of endeavour. The fact that some very poorly motivated relatively low ability doctors also go into private practice does not diminish this argument. The right of NHS doctors to do private practice is uniquely organised to encourage the very ablest doctors to continue in the NHS to the benefit of the patients they see and to the enormous benefit of the doctors they teach, and the future generations who benefit from those taught skills. This truth has been masked by the problem of doctors who fail to deliver their NHS contract. This is a separate

disciplinary matter and the role of Medical Directors in Trusts should be enhanced to ease these anxieties. The bigger danger is that Labour's political dogma on this issue has contributed to the government's current attack on the profession, which is threatening the whole public health care system.

Finally, the value of private practice should be that the patient buys access to the most experienced and able clinicians and does so with little discernable delay, (even though the reality is often different, through patient innocence and an individual doctor's well cultivated social standing within a community). All talk about better food and a private room is an irrelevant hypocrisy; a good public health care system ought to sell these anyway.

Nurses and Midwives
A guiding principle behind all staffing proposals has been to create options - choices - for staff and potential staff to maximise the ability of public health care to obtain staff and respond to the huge labour deficit. This must apply to nursing and midwifery as well.

- The same financial support to students should exist as for medicine and on the same basis.

- The NHS should return in the short term to a dual entry system for training, but retain one qualification. The new option should be direct entry from 18 years of age or older to Trust employment on a half-and-half contract such that in every two weeks one week should be worked as a paid employee of the Trust in a ward/department etc. Trusts would provide premises locally and colleges/universities would provide tuition. Time out for training could be staggered or could be am or pm etc. Night-time experience of NHS work would be a part of this. Pay for the NHS work component should at least equal basic health care assistant (HCA) rates locally in addition to the option of a grant for the training half. Trusts and Colleges jointly should be allowed to employ/enrol applicants with less than the normal academic requirements if the student was promising in other ways. Such entrants could only continue in training if they achieved quantifiable targets at the end of Year One. This 'half-time' training contract would require an extra 18 months in pre-qualifying training.

There has got to be a way of bringing the school leaver with nursing and midwifery aspirations *directly* into ward employment. If full time nursing and midwifery undergraduate courses continue to lose graduates to non-nursing employment, relative to this new option, the balance of training investment will have to change.

Nursing care is often impeded by the lack of provision of post basic training places to meet demand, eg ITU nursing, the old ENB 100. At Regional and local level there should be authority and funds to teach and be taught out of hours at standard rates of pay to avoid the worst blockages.

Other Health Care Professions

Again the same free training options and also the post qualifying training options.

v **National Service**

Not only are people in the main economic and social groups unaware of the real lives of people in other groups, but also the generations are equally separate and foreign, even within social groups. It is popular today to encourage young adults to take a gap year - indeed it has become a social cult. The result for many is a year of pleasure spent within one's own social and age group - sometimes leading to a lifetime's disinclination to the socially necessary commitment to work. Even for the socially committed young adults the experience of a year or less in the slums of Peru is unreal; and can be totally disconnected from any understanding of, or obligation to, their own society.

The time may have come when this trend should be reversed. Perhaps this gap year should be focused upon social responsibility and obligation *within* one's own society. There is a desperate shortage of support staff throughout health and social care, particularly support for the elderly. So how about trying to reduce this generational and social gap? Other forms of public service would be acceptable and for those who have too much physical energy to cope well with the elderly, perhaps a more disciplined activity would help?

5 Conclusion

For many readers committed to the provision of health care within the NHS some of the proposals in this Chapter will appear "challenging", but together they constitute a logically coherent way of trying to regenerate the public health care system.

- A free at the point of delivery health care system funded out of taxation can *never* escape its core requirement to achieve *equality* of provision. The right of Foundation Trusts to be better than other trusts, the right of so-called high performing trusts to have *extra* freedom and resources; the right of local populations to fight over single issue health agendas to the relative *discrimination* against other local service users is all contrary to this commitment to equality. For this reason alone it has to be rejected.

If we wanted many different local health care systems unlike one another it would be more equitable to use an insurance system so that every individual had some basic control of what they needed for themselves. But the need for genuine equality for the UK population goes much further than sweeping away the PR inventions of New Labour. It has to address fifty years of failing to provide a geographically and socially balanced provision of service. The return of Regions and their ability to address this balance in the short term is vital if a free at the point of delivery system is to survive. The political will to tackle Glasgow, the most gross resource imbalance in the UK, will be a measure of whether national equality might be achievable. If the government fails, a new government will be required; if all political parties fail then free at the point of delivery health care funded out of taxation will fail as well.

- The provision of a modern acute hospital for each half million people, with identical core services, goes a long way to achieve the equality identified above. The actual population size appropriate to modern acute hospital provision is no revelation to the government or the medical establishment. The reasoning has been public for the last six years and known about for longer. But for success in implementation a government is required that will share this knowledge with the public and *lead from the front* in achieving a consensus for change.

- The present policy whereby the physical structure of public health provision can be farmed out to the private sector, whilst retaining direct control over those who work in clinical care through direct employment, does need turning upside down. The staff are the key resource, they alone can decide whether, in the next decade, they will go the extra mile for public health care or not. They have to be liberated and empowered to achieve the necessary productivity leap and be rewarded for it. But they must not be compelled to do so; choice is necessary for all staff to ensure that all can contribute in whatever ways they find appropriate. The facilities and environment within which they work must be brought up to new standards as quickly as possible; must be governed by the commitment to equality of national provision and must last for more than thirty years. The 'pick and choose' of PFI could not possibly achieve this and must be immediately replaced by *well managed* public build.

- Purchasing and commissioning has become a modern day blind spot. Think about it! What purpose does it serve! It prevents GPs from referring patients that need to be referred; it stops hospitals performing work that needs to be performed and it spawns a massive bureaucracy that spends every year negotiating "prices" that don't need to exist let alone be negotiated. A properly established performance measurement and performance management (PMM) of health care workload supervised within a management framework that can challenge outcomes, set targets and call hospitals to account is all the Treasury needs. If GP referrals make waiting lists longer we are nearer the truth and know where to act. Equally if Trusts are unable to learn from the PMM successes of others and fail to achieve performance *when equally resourced*, the NHS Management Board and the Region should know where to act to promote quality and output. All that is needed is that PMM is strengthened, made comprehensive and linked to a new national coding that will identify *all* the services that can be provided free of charge on the NHS. The funding of all Trusts by actual population and clinical output then matches resources to populations to close the loop.

The withdrawal of PCTs, also restores *genuine* choice to patients. It restores the crucial importance of the GP/patient relationship in allowing patients to choose *for themselves* the health treatment they wish to pursue and where they go to get good and/or timely treatment. At a stroke it frees *individual* patients from the tyranny of single-issue health politics that is now set to dominate PCT policy. But GPs will have to clarify what is available within the NHS framework and what is outside it; so that waiting lists

157

become genuine measures of actual un-met demand. The New NHS sees this *individual* freedom of choice as impossible due to the failure of GP supply. Other recommendations in this chapter address the GP shortage

But what matters most is empowering staff to organise, to innovate, to achieve and to be rewarded. Without this piece of the jigsaw puzzle the labour supply deficit will bring the current system down around Ministers' ears. The government must stop believing their own daily rhetoric about labour supply achievement. They must give up their battle to 'subdue' the medical profession. Most of all they must stop inventing a new policy gimmick to respond to each new revelation of labour supply inadequacy: all too often a gimmick that never gets much further than its date of announcement.

The public is not being told about the appalling labour crisis in the NHS. A very recent example in early 2003 was the GP survey that showed nearly a quarter of GPs seriously considering retirement within five years. If half of these intentions cannot be changed in the next two or three years the NHS GP service will collapse in several parts of the UK. The government's response to this news was to put out an immediate statement that more GPs were now in training than at any time in the past, expressing confidence and *implying* that this would meet the threat. Even if all those in training qualify as soon as possible and take up full time jobs in NHS general practice it would in no way prevent a national supply crisis if nearly a quarter of GPs do go within five years.

The government is well aware of this. Do they have a fall back position other than that of Wilkins Micawber? If they do it is probably to substitute even more nurses for doctors in general practice. And if they do this and further denude hospital nursing they further exacerbate the hospital nursing supply crisis. When will the public realise they are being slipped across from GP doctors to GP nurses -

and will they eventually realise and rebel? The only long term solution is the one put forward in the chapter. The GPs have to be given a future, in a new NHS, that will be conducive to the proper practice of medicine so that GPs will stay long enough to save the service for a new generation of doctors. This solution, like so many in this chapter, is strictly time limited.

In hospital medicine the supply issue is made more dramatic by the deadline of August 1st 2004 for implementing the EU Working Time Directive. If the government fails to suspend the Directive the national acute hospital service will begin to implode on that date. The government's failure to beat the consultants into submitting to the 'New NHS' contract is already beginning to run-down hospital consultant medical supply irrespective of August 1st 2004. Dr Reid's appointment, with authority to backtrack on the consultants contract, may prove to be yet another initiative in the list of desperate stop-gap measures. But a First World health service *cannot* be provided by imported non-consultant career grade doctors.

If nothing happens in two to three years except more and irrelevant gimmicks the option to save a medically provided health service will disappear. Medical general practice will then increasingly become a private service to the better off, with nurses looking after the rest. Hospital medical practice will become increasingly imported career grade doctors with the specialist consultants doing more and more private practice. If this happens the government will finally have killed off the NHS, killed off equality and probably killed off some of the patients as well. This book has sought to show that there is an alternative - but if the change is not started upon soon the worsening labour supply crisis will finally close the option.